Tommy,

Great me[?] for the support. Hope you enjoy the book. Blame the typos on RJ!

Best,

[signature]

1

Hero Sandwich

A true story

by John Cerqueira

Brooklyn Roach Press

A Division of Brooklyn Roach

Multimedia, Inc.

New York

2006

For more information, please visit us

on the web:

www.Hero-Sandwich.com

www.BrooklynRoach.com

Hero Sandwich: A True Story by John Cerqueira is the recounting of the events of Mr. Cerqueira's life by Mr. Cerqueira, to the very best of his ability.

Many of the events in this book occurred under less than desirable conditions for complete technical accuracy, while either under great duress, stress, or under the influence of many, many cocktails.

At some points within the book some names have been changed or omitted, this has been done at the discretion of the author so as really not to hurt anyone's feelings. Similarly, the opinions represented within the pages of this book are those of the author and in no way represent the beliefs or practices of Brooklyn Roach Multimedia.

Some of the recollected conversations and announcements have not come from exact transcripts, but were paraphrased to the best recollection of the author. The essence of these sentiments or introductions have maintained their integrity, and the author by no means makes any kind of public statement regarding any of the mentioned persons except to further the story.

For more information, please contact Brooklyn Roach Multimedia Inc., 801 Motor Parkway, Suite 200, Hauppauge, NY 11788 or write to rojoroach@brooklynroach.com.

Front and back cover designs and layout by Lisa Ferguson, who rocks, by the way.

Edited by R.J. Wafer, who also rocks, by the way.

Library of Congress Cataloging-in-Publication Data

John Cerqueira, 1979- hopefully a very, very long time from now. *Hero Sadnwich: A true story* by John Cerqueira.

ISBN 1-59872-703-6
$14.99 paperback.

This book is dedicated to the men and women that were lost that fateful day. I mourn your loss every day, and pJay for your families and loved ones.

. . . and to the members of the NYFD and the NYPD who risked all and lost their lives to deliver thousands of people to safety.

. . . and to the men and women that have given their lives to protect us all since. For you I am eternally grateful and pJay that God will keep you safe from harm.

-John

Chapters

Hero Sandwich

A true story

by John Cerqueira

Hero, noun, 1. A figure in mythology or legend renowned for great strength, courage and daring. 2. A man celebrated for special achievements and attributes. 3. The leading male character in a story or play. 4. *Slang*. A long split sandwich roll containing a variety of fillings.

Sandwich, noun, 1. Two or more slices of bread with a filling, as meat, between them. 2. Something resembling a sandwich. –verb. To insert between two other things, especially tightly.

Down

The only light I see is from one single flashlight in a long dark corridor, it moves sporadically back and forth. I don't feel how strained my forearms might be burning from the front of the wheelchair's weight in my right hand.

What I can feel is the cold calf deep water that has collected on this floor from the building's sprinkler system. I'm not sure what floor we're on but we started at the 81st, tower one, and it seems like we're close to the bottom since the firefighters leading us seem to be trying to figure something out.

Our line of 30 people moves in one direction, stops, then we turn back the way we just came. Surely we're almost out. Not quite, we stop again.

"What's the story Chief?" I hear a younger firefighter say.

"Shut up I'm thinking" Chief says.

"Yeah, but how do we get out of here?", "I… uh… I'm not sure".

Not sure? "Whoa," I say "whoa guys, you came in here somehow right, why not just go back that way"…silence…suddenly my eyes are blinded by the flashlight now in my face.

"Just hold the flashlight kid." Chief hands the flashlight to me and I point it the first way we tried to get out. I hear banging on the steel door, then a flood of light.

We're out, thank you God we're…what the?! The lobby is completely destroyed. Turnstiles blown out near the walls, counters cracked in half, doors off hinges, floor to ceiling plate glass windows broken. What captures my attention the most is the desolate West Side Highway, the thick coat of what looks like new fallen snow. Something like a Norman Rockwell painting with red nosed kids sledding and throwing snowballs. I come to from my Rockwell dreamland by the sound of what sounds like a car wreck, and then another… 'what the hell is that?' I look around to see where it's coming from. Before I can figure it out I hear the approaching sound of a distorted two way radio and a voice from behind me. "Well, go on, you guys head out the window." I look back at the older firefighter, he waves us forward, and Mike and I head toward the ground floor window with Tina.

The car wreck sound continues, crashes sounding around us.

We step through the window onto this "snow" which is thick and feels like feathers under my feet and seems the consistency of flour. We put Tina in the ambulance. She begins to cry. Mike gives her a business card. "Ok sweetheart, when you get where you're going you give me a call".

"Thank you both". The ambulance doors slam shut.

"Alright" I say, "Where to?"

Mike looks around, taking in the scene, "Up town, I guess, right?"

"Yeah" I say, " Let's move" My eyes follow Mike's and I see the flames from the top of the building. To my right a piece of the waffle like façade of the building is standing straight up after crushing the Marriott that stood next door.

Holy shit, all of this on the ground has got to be ash from the fire upstairs, all from some poor bastard that probably had a heart attack and ran is prop plane into the biggest most hard to miss building in the city!

"Mike, let's get the hell out of here before we get "penny-off-the-empire state-buildinged" by a computer or a paper weight."

Mike is in a daze. "Wait a second, I just want to go back and see…" all of a sudden out of nowhere a man appears. Something doesn't seem right about him.

"Yeah Mike," he says, "let's go back." Mike's gaze toward the building breaks and he looks at the guy, "wait, how do you…"

"Let's go Mike!!" I say "We have got to move!"

"OK" he says, "but let's just see if everyone from the office is out."

"Mike! We're the last ones from the…" I look up and my eye catches an image moving from the top of the building. It appears to fall slowly. As it comes closer I make out the figure. It's a person, a man, in a suit, falling, no, throwing himself to his death.

I follow with my eyes until he falls behind a building. I never see him hit the ground but hear the newly recognizable car wreck sound. I feel like the wind has been knocked out of me.

"Holy shit Mike." I hear the sound again and once more, "that sound is people. People falling. People jumping. We have got to get…" before I can finish, Mike's eyes pop open, his face drops, he turns and uses the legs conditioned to be a Brown running back almost 20 years ago. He's gone, and officially the fastest white guy I've ever seen up close. I look up at the top of World Trade Center One. It looks like a cascade or an avalanche. This fucking building is peeling away right above us. I turn and follow Mike as well as I can. Sure, I'm 15 years younger but I'm also 30 pounds heavier, plus in my defense I was on crutches a week ago after spraining my ankle playing volleyball.

I run as fast as I've ever run. I run like Ed Norton in Fight club but don't have enough time for my legs to burn. I look behind me… 'fuck, why can't I go faster? This dust cloud is behind me and gaining like a monster in a bad dream'

It's getting closer, I pump my arms, my ankle pops, I don't care, I'm running for my life. I'm losing, I'm not going to make it. Find cover. There is none. Just my luck here on the West Side Highway to be in the only place in this crowded bitch of a city with no cover when I'M running from this cloud of death. Wait, there's a news van with a guy peeking out from behind. Well, it's not ideal, but you know the thing about beggars being choosy. I yell to the guy "Get the hell out of the way! Get behind the truck!" I run into him at full speed and grab him to brace myself. I pull him with me behind the van and duck...ONE FULL SECOND...then, roaring, getting louder, closer.

The van shakes violently. I hold on and press my back against the van as best as I can. The windows break, debris sounds like bullets on the metal. I try to take a deep breath. I can't. Oh, God, this isn't just dust. It's hot, thick debris. I've taken a deep breath of concrete, asbestos, and ash. It's lodged in my throat. I can't breathe. I can't even close my mouth. I can't hear. Why can't I breathe? Shit! I can't breath. Is this it God? Am I done? I'm only 22 years old. What about my parents? My unborn kids? Shit, I still can't breathe, it hurts to try. 'OK God, I'm Yours, let's do it.' What will my funeral be like? Will I go to heaven? OK, try to breath one more time...no dice. I miss you Mom, I miss you Dad, I love you both...Alright God, do Your thing.

Julie

Every guy like me has at one point in his life, a cool girl friend that he hangs out with. This is the 'anything goes' girl. The guy can say anything he wants, do anything he wants, be whatever he wants because the nature of the relationship dictates that any judgment the girl makes of him is inconsequential since neither one of the two have any intentions of making the relationship romantic. The guy's version... 'Who cares, not like I'm trying to get her in the sack..' The girl's version, 'Oh we're just friends, I wouldn't want to ruin that.'

      The ass kicker of this situation is that the two members of this party end up spending more time with one another than they might with any true significant others or even their friends of the same sex. The reasons being are that they are

      (1) More comfortable and fun to be around than someone you start dating and

      (2) You can actually go do date type things when you don't have anything better to do but you really would actually be with that person anyway.

There are three, and only three, ways that two, single, heterosexual members of the opposite sex can maintain such a relationship (as evidenced by a slew of John Hughes movies).

(1) The girl is not physically attracted to the guy.

(2) The guy is not physically attracted to the girl. Or...

(3) The two are equally attracted to one another but both are too chicken shit to admit it for fear of rejection, or the infamous feeling weird.

Julie is a well educated, well-shaped, southern blonde, with big blue eyes and a gorgeous face, and I have to say that I'm not too hard on the eyes either. So, our relationship fell into the third category.

Julie and I, although having gone to rival high schools, didn't really meet until freshman year of college. Her roommate and my roommate were in a serious high school to college relationship that was on the outs, so we spent a lot of time together while the two occupied one of our respective rooms with their romantic, post adolescent, *Dawson's Creek/ Wonder Years*, battles. She had a boyfriend at the time and I was running wild as an 18 year old thrown into a world of no rules from mom and dad, co-ed living, an environment where girls' libidos were almost always stronger than their judgment. Neither Julie, nor I looked to one another to fill any romantic or physical void and a strong friendship developed.

We spent a lot of time together, talked about everything, and when her sorority had a function she would normally bring me as her date since I was the best alternative to the other frat boys that wanted to get her in the sack, and we'd always have a good time. We would dance, have a great time, sometimes go home together, eat pizza and pass out.

I met her parents when it came time for us to move out of the freshmen dorm, I helped her folks with the move.

"Ooh Julie! Who is this good looking young man!?"

"Hi, ma'am my name is John Cerqueira." She shakes my hand like an old south debutant.

"Pleasure to meet you John." Then she turns to Julie, "Well this strapping boy looks like he'll make an excellent addition to the gene pool!" She winks at me, to let me know she's joking, kind of.

"Mom!!!" Julie was mortified, but this isn't the last time people mistook our relationship to be something it wasn't…yet.

Our friendship grew over the next few years of college. We became close with each other's families, becoming fixtures at birthdays, holidays, vacations, still acting as complete friends. Julie even drove up to New York City with Todd and me to move me up right after graduation. I didn't expect the scene that would follow as they were leaving.

"Alright guys! Thanks for helping me. I love this place! I can't wait to start doing everything!" Yes, staring my new life in the face had me speaking like a sales girl at the Gap.

"Yeah," Todd says, "You can expect me to visit at least once a month starting next week, buddy."

"I hope you're paying rent, asshole." We all laugh, well two of us at least. I look to Julie and she has tears in her eyes. I've never seen her cry in the 4 years I've known her.

"Jules? Jules, what's wrong?"

She tries to talk but stops, looks up toward the sky and starts fanning her face with her hand to try to stop herself from the sobbing to come.

"Jules? Sweetie? Hey," my voice changes like I'm consoling a child, "It's not like I'm dying. I'm just moving 8 hours up the road. We can all hang out as much as we want." It's not making her better, maybe even worse. "Hey, look at me."
I gently direct her face so her eyes lock on mine. When they do, her face contorts into the preamble to an emotional eruption and then, waterworks.

She is sobbing uncontrollably, like a child throwing a tantrum in a grocery store. Todd and I look at each other not knowing what to do. What the hell is going on here? Who gets this upset about one of their friends moving?

I was that oblivious.

"Dude, I told you." Todd and I are on the phone the night after.

"No way, man we're just friends. We have been for years."

"Well, all I know is that I didn't start boo-hooing when we were leaving."

"Yeah, but that's just because you can tell I hate you."

"Fuck you. Dude, she didn't stop until we were almost to south Jersey."

"Alright, whatever. Maybe she does, but I just moved to the city, she's got 3 years of law school wherever she decides to go. Not that I've not thought about it, but...I don't know, this sounds like a cop out, but she's really important to me, what if this really messes things up. I don't know if I want to take that chance."

That New City Smell

I love living in this city. The energy, the history, the nightlife, I
love it all. I think this as I head downtown to meet Todd and his
boss, both in town from Atlanta, for drinks. Todd's boss Tom
started a consulting company, Aslan Training and Development,
dealing in sales and sales management training. I haven't seen
Todd in a while, love meeting successful people that start their own
company, and am always up for a little happy hour drink. All in all,
should be a good time.

     I appreciate how little I have to walk from the 9 train to the
restaurant to minimize my outside time in this steamy August heat.
I bask in the blast of cold air that hits me as I pop into Sushi Samba.
I look to my right and see Todd and who I assume to be Tom at the
bar.

     "What's up buddy! How are things?" I say as I reach in for
the customary handshake/hug/violent heterosexual male back
beating greeting of an old friend.

     "Not much man. Hey, this is Tom."

"Pleasure." I reach out to shake hands. "Great to finally meet you."

"Likewise. Now I can put a face with a name for all of the stories Todd tells me about frat life at NC State." Tom turns to Todd, "Todd he's not *that* ugly, and you don't even notice the halitosis."

OK we have a jokester on our hands. I'm glad this isn't a typical 'meet the boss' night where I try to impress some stuffy old bastard. This guy actually seems cool.

Tom is a tall, about 6' 3" and thin, maybe 180. I'm surprised that he's in his mid forties since his dark hair isn't the least bit gJay and his face looks like he's looked that way since a teenager. He still has a bit of an awkward demeanor but he pulls it off as charming. Our conversation flows smoothly, with jokes, some work talk, and talk of the differences between Atlanta and New York…the many, many differences, all made easier with the social lubricant of alcohol.

"Alright New Yorkers," (Todd lived in NY for a summer so Tom is referring to both of us) "Where do you recommend next?"

I turn to Todd, shrug my shoulders, "I dunno. How 'bout Swift over in the East Village, it's just a quick cab ride unless you want to walk in this hellish heat."

We head out to hail a cab after Tom graciously pays the tab. We're all a bit toasted already and we let Tom do his best New Yorker cab hailer impression and we get a cab almost instantly. We load into the cab, close the door and hear one of the automated messages for safety. This one was Dennis Franz from NYPD Blue in his brash Chicago accent "Hi, This is Dennis Franz, don't forget to buckle your safety belt."

Evidently the powers that be decided it is better not to have cabbies talk anymore. Tom snickers as this is one of the first times he's heard this, and then the cab is off. We peel off just short of warp speed, very reminiscent of Buster Poindexter as the Ghost of Christmas past in Bill MurJay's *Scrooged*. He decides to take Bleecker eastbound, on which I was unaware that the speed limit was over 60 miles an hour. We give each other an 'oh shit' look and Tom leans forward and yells over the French Moroccan talk radio, "Sir, we're in a bit of a hurry so could you go a little faster?"

Todd and I roar with laughter and this has been officially the funniest thing I've ever heard Tom say. I've yet to tell the story successfully so that anyone else thinks so, and may have failed again now, so if so, just chalk it up to having had to be there

We arrive at Swift to sit down over some Caffrey's and although I wasn't intending to do the verbal resume, we get into what I do for a living. Little did I know that Tom was interviewing me.

"So John, how is selling at Network Plus going?"

"Great, I hit the phones hard, set my appointments, and keep closing deals. Money's good and I can't believe that I get to make a living out of talking and solving problems."

"So what's your biggest challenge with this sale?"

"Well, telecom is pretty much a commodity and there are a lot of companies that do it, so you just have to have a pretty tough skin and be persistent. I mean, I'm calling on people who have heard the same thing a million times that day and I have to figure out a way to read them and connect with them in the 10 seconds they have to decide whether they listen to me or hang up…and believe me in Manhattan you get hung up on a lot and that's if you're lucky and they don't scream at you to take them off of your list. I don't even know what the hell list they're talking about!"

Can you say 'typical sales guy' conversation? Thankfully no one quotes Mamet.

"Wow, well what's the worst part? Is it the rejection?"

"No, not really, I don't mind the rejection. If one doesn't work go to the next, there is an infinite number of businesses in this town. The part I don't like about it is the fact that the sale is quick and kind of mindless. You try to sell on value, but at the end of the day, these people want to talk about price. It just gets a little old and I've only been doing it a couple of months."

"Well what do you like most about it?"

"The win. I love the win. I love *to* win. It's a pretty cool feeling to turn someone from hating my guts because I bothered their busy day or their time wasting on the internet, to getting them to sign on the dotted line, put them in a better situation, and head to the bank with my commission. Yeah, it's the win."

I didn't know it but I just earned myself a job. Tom asked that night if I'd ever consider moving to Atlanta to do business development for his consulting group.

"I appreciate it, but I find it hard to believe that I'm going to get tired of this place any time soon."

Black, Brown & Empty

"Hey I'm heading down to walk around Soho in a little bit. Wanna come with?"

"Karri, it's so damn hot. Let's go to a nice air conditioned café somewhere, or go sit by the peers where there's at least a breeze."

"Come on you big baby it will be fun."

"Fine, I'll meet you at Broadway and Spring in an hour." Karri is a friend of mine from home, she's in college at Parson's School of Design. She's a tiny little girl, even for her age, with straight brown hair.

"Yay, I'll see you there!" In case you couldn't tell, she's also quite chipper.

"Alright, it is hot, let's pop in here."

I pull Karri into a leather shop. Not chains and whips, jackets and purses.

I've been looking to get a black leather jacket for the fall and I figure I can probably get a pretty good deal since it's above 90 degrees despite our getting further into September. I don't expect that they'll be flying off the shelves.

I find one I like and talk the shop owner down to just about as reasonable a price as I would expect. Thank you Economics professor for teaching me the effect demand has on market price. I walk out of the store pretty happy with my purchase.

Back at home, the more I look at the jacket the less happy I am with it. I thought I was buying a black jacket but in weird lighting it kind of looks like it has a brown hue to it. It's so close. Up until now I was absolutely certain it was black. I decide to run some comparative analysis on this issue by hanging the jacket on the doorway right under the hall light and pulling every black article of clothing out of my closet.

I start with the leather gloves. Made of the same material, I figure that this would give me the most accurate assessment. But one second it looks close enough and the next it looks completely different. I try the same test with a black sweater. Not really that close, but it's a different material. Maybe the light just hits it differently. Shoes... hmm... Pants... can't tell. I can't seem to come to a definitive answer. I decide to enlist another pair of eyes to help me judge.

"Richard!" I yell to the other room. "Hey, come here for a second will ya?"

My roommate Richard is in his room playing video games. Richard's parents are from Thailand but he was born and raised in Plano, TX. I have to say, I'm taken a little off guard, even in this day and age to hear anyone of Asian descent speak with a thick

Southern accent. Richard is nice enough, but one of those guys you have to check for a pulse once in a while.

"Hey buddy, "I hold up all of the test pieces of clothing to the jacket, "What do you think?" I alternate articles now to give him a better view. "Does this jacket seem black, or just really dark brown to you?"

Richard steps back, crosses his arms, and places one hand to his face to stroke his chin in a way that makes me think that he is thinking just as hard about this predicament as I am. He doesn't say anything for what I estimate to be about 5 seconds. Then...

"Do you mean to tell me that for the last 20 minutes this is what you've been doing?"

I nod proudly, still with an arJay of gloves, scarves, pants, and sweaters in my hands.

"Is this *really* the biggest problem you have right now?"

I pause to think, eyes looking up to the imaginary place where my brain finds answers.

"Yup, sure is...now what do you think?"

Richard walks away, almost in disgust at the attention I pay to the most minute issues.

Screw him. He was playing Zelda but *I* am the asshole.

I yell to him in the other room, "Well I'm probably going to return it!!"

He doesn't answer.

I look at the receipt for the jacket to see if it says whether I can return it or not.

All purchases are final
Date of Purchase: 9/10/01

The blind leading the. . . oh forget it.

"So you'll be there?"

"Yeah Ma, I'll be there."

"Ok baby, make sure you're there by 7:30. Everyone at work just can't wait to meet you and hear your story. We have the largest conference room booked and the responses have everyone in the department coming. I'm so proud of you."

"Thanks Ma. I have to go do this speaking think at the school for the blind so I gotta run. Love you."

"Ooh. . . What are you wearing?"

"Funny Ma, real funny."

"What? I didn't mean it like that, now you've made me feel bad."

"Whatever. You wonder where I get it. Really, I have to go."

"Alright baby, I love you."

An hour later I walk out of the Moorehead School for the Blind after a less than riveting speech that everyone treated like I was JFK or Dr. King. I still can't understand why people want me to talk to their groups about 9/11.

It's not that I'm uncomfortable in front of groups. The truth is I kind of like the attention. It's just that, I get that it is a big event and my story is extraordinary, but I'm just not comfortable telling it any other manor than in a bar with some friends as the story doesn't seem to have any point that I can easily communicate. I learned from public speaking classes that great speeches of this nature tend to have a call to action; but who the hell am I to tell people what to do? I'm a 22 year old punk kid who got lucky and was in the right/wrong place at the right/wrong time. I always feel guilty that they're expecting some inspirational Tony Robbins presentation and all they get is me telling a story. Hey, people ask me to speak and I feel that I owe something after being so lucky, so I go and no matter what I say, the audience and the MC are always gracious.

I just don't get it. . .

All this fuss over me.

Impact

"That's two bucks, Cerqueira!!" I hear from the burly, shorn-headed Staten Islander sitting at the first desk in the office.

Shit! Rienstein. That bastard always catches me when I'm late.

Tardiness had become a problem in recent months so Mike, the Branch Manager of the New York office of Network Plus had instilled a new means of punishment for being late. Anyone who came in even a minute after our 8:30 start time had to contribute two dollars to the pot and supposedly the proceeds would be used for a company sponsored happy hour. You'd think that this would act as a deterrent to being late but it just ended up being another two bucks that I would add to the price of my breakfast. Often, I enjoyed said breakfast with a healthy helping of embarrassment served up by Mark Reinstein who was always there early, announcing my late arrival in the middle of the office, just in case Mike didn't notice.

I pull out the two dollars in change, which had been the little 'screw you' the habitual late comers developed in protest of this policy, and I slunk to my desk and get ready for my sales calls for the day. It's only 8:32, two minutes past start time.

My buddy Matt leans over to me from his desk next to mine in the call pit. "Don't worry Johnny, he's just being a prick since you're the new guy."

"New? I've been here for 3 months. I think he's just a prick."

"Don't worry about it man." Matt pulls out an apartment broker's listing. We had been planning to move in together with another guy, Ryan, who worked with us. "Hey, check this out. It's the floor plan of the place we looked at yesterday. It's such a big one bedroom that we can split the actual bedroom into two, and then part of the living room as another. This way, the $3000 split between the three of us will only be $1000 each." Matt smiles like the math is a magic trick. "Dude, this place is right across from Sutton Place, Turtle Bay, Opal…It's the friggin' Long Island Sorority girl meat market!"

"Alright dude," I concede, "this would be pretty cool. I'm just not sure how I'm going to come up with the first and last month's rent and then the broker's fee."

"Just think about it OK? I can't stand Staten Island any more. And living at home is killing me!"

"Alright, I'll think about it." I get up from my desk. "But I'm not promising anything."

"Think hard, roomie!"

I walk away with my fingers in my ears, pretending not to hear Matt's most recent attempt at peer pressure. I head out of the office intending to head towards the bathroom. In my unsuccessful rush to get to work on time, I forgot to go before I got into the office. I'm still a little tired after staying up to watch the Giants game that went into overtime the night before. My sleep deprived daze makes me oblivious to the fact that I'm heading into the first open door, which is the elevator, rather than my intended destination.

I see my buddy Scott walk down the hall.

"Johnny boy! What's going on brother!"

"Yo Scott, how you doing man?"

"Good. Where the hell are you going already?"

I look around at my surroundings and realize that I'm in the elevator. I step out just as the doors are beginning to close. "Thanks buddy, I was trying to head towards the bathroom."

Scott scrunches his face in confusion, "In the elevator?"

"Don't ask man," I say as I walk away, "I'm just beat... need some coffee. . . quickly."

"G'morning gentlemen." Art and Mitch are in the bathroom too. It's kind of been the gathering place for getting ready for the day. The summer has been so hot that most of the guys had been making their commute without their tie's and jackets on, so we usually head to the bathroom to get presentable before the day begins. The second week in September has proven pretty mild, but the habit of the morning bathroom congregation is fading slowly.

"What's up big guy? You doing alright?"

"Yeah, Art. Just a little exhausted. I just got in."

"Oh shit," Mitch chimes in, "did Rienstein bust your balls?"

"Of course he did. What a prick."

"Don't worry about it man. It's just 'cause you're the new…"

I don't remember if I heard it, felt it, or saw the tiles flying off the bathroom wall from the impact first.

At 8:48 am on Tuesday September 11, 2001, American Airlines Flight 11 slammed into the upper floors of World Trade Center One, but for those of us who never saw it coming, our minds fathomed at first a broken elevator, or maybe a bomb and then…

"Oh my God, get in the doorway! I've been through lots of these!" Mitch yells over the sound of the continuous explosion. He lives in Brooklyn now, but grew up in San Francisco.
"We're in Manhattan! We don't have earthquakes in…" But I can't think of a better idea, and the debris from the ceiling threatens to cave in. I join Mitch and Art in the doorway and after a few seconds, the violent shaking and the noise of this unknown explosion subsides.

"What the hell was that?" I look around us. The bathroom floor is littered with broken tile and glass from the mirrors. The hallway is filling with smoke, fluorescent light bulb tubes swing from the ceiling, the drywall of the walls is collapsing on the floor covered with carpet that has been bowed from the impact.

Before either of the guys can answer me, we hear something, someone. "Hey!! Help me!" A women's voice says from the bathroom. "I can't get out of here!"

The three of us cautiously walk toward the women's bathroom not sure if anything else is going to fall on us. "Don't worry!" Mitch yells in an unsure voice of someone still processing this catastrophe, "We'll get help! Just sit tight."

"How are we going to…" I'm interrupted by a hand grabbing me violently by the shoulders. I turn around to see some dude that looks like an IT guy.

"Let's go man, we have to move!" He grabs me and I don't have the physical or mental energy to argue. I'm lead from the commotion in the hallway into a pristine office that, other than the mass of people freaking out, appears to not have been affected at all by the now mysterious explosion. Once we get in the office, this guy turns me around by my shoulders to face him.

"Listen here! An airplane has just hit the building. Don't worry, but the floors above us are on fire. We just have to hang out here for a few and wait for instructions from downstairs."

Oprah Wants Me

I fumble for the phone from the space on the floor on which I assume that I passed out last night. "Uh, hel...hello." Whew, that's a hung-over cigarette voice if I ever heard one.

"Hello John?" says a fairly feminine yet decidedly male voice that I don't remember hearing before (but then again I did mention that I drank enough last night not to remember how I got on the floor).

"Yeah, this is John." I say, alternating between squinting and opening my eyes wide in order to focus on the VCR clock. 8:30 in the morning! Who the hell is this?

"Hi John, this is Jay from the Oprah Winfrey show." Who? From the what now?

"Yeah right, who is this for real, Derek is this you?" Damn he does a good queen voice.

"Um no this is Jay from Oprah, is this a bad time?"

OK, I'll go with it.

"No, this is a perfect time, what can I do for you?"

"Well," he begins in what sounds like a valley girl voice, ending his sentences with a voice inflection that makes everything he says sound like a question. "Ms. Winfrey heard about your story? And, she was really touched? And she would love for you and your boss Michael to be on the show?"

Seriously?

"Seriously? The show? Let me get this straight. You want *us* to be on the Oprah show."

"Well, that is, of course, unless you're not free to fly to Chicago early next week."

Well let's see, I'm unemployed, not in school, living with my parents and spend every night getting bombed with my friends. Hmm let me check my schedule . . .

"No Jay, I think I'm open."

"Wonderful, she'll be so happy to hear that."

"OK, so uh, how do we do this?"

"Oh my assistant will send you an itinerary. You just get on the plane at RDU and we'll have a limo come to pick you up at the airport in Chicago."

"Sounds good to me. Anything else?"

"Actually yes. Ms. Winfrey really likes to be the first show to have high profile stories, so we'd really appreciate it if you refrain from making any other nationally televised appearances." High profile? Oh yeah, that's the paparazzi at my door right now.

"Well I don't really think that will be a problem, but sure thing."

"Well great then I'll see you in a few days!"

Ha! How do you like that? The Oprah Winfrey show. Wait until everybody gets a load of this one.

I just get back to falling asleep and my cell phone rings again with a New York number on caller ID.

"Hello?"

"Yes is this John Cer…Cerq…"

"Yeah, Cerqueira. What can I do for you?"

"This is Helen, from Good Morning America."

Get the hell outta here! It's like I'm friggin' Tom Cruise!

"Hey, Helen."

"John, we here at GMA have heard your story and think it's fantastic! How would you like to come back to New York and be interviewed with your boss by Charlie Gibson tomorrow?"

"That sounds great but…" Jay said don't do any other national TV.

"But what?"

"Nothing. I'd love to." Hey, how many times in my life am I going to get to be on national television?

"Great, just give me your email and we can have an itinerary to you in an hour or so. Is it OK if you leave tonight."

Again, let me check my schedule.

"Yes that will be fine."

"Great! I'll see you tomorrow morning!"

What the hell is going on here? Oprah, Good Morning America. This is starting to get a little ridiculous. Maybe I could make a living on per diems on the talk show circuit. . .

"Ladies and gentlemen we are preparing for landing at New York's LaGuardia Airport. Please turn off any electronics and return your tJay tables and seat backs to their upright position."

I look out the window to my right. I always get a kick out of flying over the city. The water, the Statue of Liberty, the lower tip of Manhattan, and the…the big…smoldering pile of debris where the World Trade Center used to be. I'm sick and I get a blinding headache. This is definitely a different New York.

It's been over two weeks and I can still smell what I recognize to be the odor from what the media has now dubbed Ground Zero. I quickly realize that this is not going to be a particularly fun trip to what used to be my favorite place in the world.

I grab a cab to my hotel, drop, my stuff in the room and run out to meet my friends Cindy and Jason for dinner. If one thing is going to be the same it's the vibrant nightlife of Manhattan right?

Yeah, not so much.

"Good evening welcome to Carmines. My name is Sarah. Can I start you guys off with any drinks?"

Her voice echo's of the hardwoods of the place in which we are the only table. Hell, the only people other than the bartender, our waitress, and another guy who I can't tell what he does since there aren't any other customers to do whatever he does for.

"Where is everybody?" I ask the waitress.

The "I'm working for your tip" demeanor drains from her face.

"It's been really tough the last couple of weeks…for everybody."

Cindy looks down

"You can't imagine John, the whole city is depressed."

"Well *we* are not going to be. *We* still have a lot to be happy about." I turn to the waitress. "We'll have a bottle of Pinot Noir please."

"It's been really hard here John," Cindy starts, "A girl in my office lost her roommate down there. And it seems like almost everyone who is from this area knows someone who died that day. It's just…" she starts to tear up. "I watched those building come down from Times Square. That could have been you and I can't… I can't think…" she can't get the words out.

"Shhh," I put my arm around her and she buries her head into my shoulder. "I know sweetheart, but I'm here." I whisper, "I'm right here."

She squeezes me tight.

"I don't know what I would have done if…"

The wine comes. I waive off the waitress's offer for a tasting before she pours and grab the bottle myself and begin to poor. The waitress doesn't need to be part of this little scene. I dish out the full glasses to Cindy and then to Jason and I raise my glass for a toast. The two follow suit.

"To those who didn't make it....and to those who did. Salut!"

"Salut!"

Suffice it to say that even a depressed New York is still a good place to go out and have a night of drinking. . . that makes it pretty hard to get up by 6:00 in the morning to be in the ABC green room by 6:30. I think the poor girl in makeup had to pull out the stuff used in *Thriller* to cover up the bags under my eyes.

The entire show is a blur. The hangover, combined with my difficulty talking about what had happened, the make-up and my newfound camera fright, makes me look like something out of Mme. Taussaud's Wax Museum. Mike does most of the talking and poor Charlie Gibson tries just about everything to get me to say something. Anything. When I do speak, it sounds like a mumble coming out of my mouth, stiff with nervousness and dehydration, and I only defer to Mike anyhow. Oh well:

Camera Fright- 1
John- 0

Getting in Trouble

"Hello!"

"Johnny C! What's up buddy, it's Josh." It's my little brother in the fraternity. I'm back in Raleigh only 5 months after my graduation and two months after 9/11, most of my friends are still here and it's been, thankfully, very easy to slip back into life back home. Even easier now that I'm not in school, not working, and in full swing of my little 15 minutes.

"What's up kid? How are things?"

"Great! Hey it's my 21st today and we're all going to Crowley's later on. Wanna come buy me a shot or 8?"

"Oh shit, wow, that's tempting buddy, but I have to wake up early tomorrow to go speak at my mom's company."

"Who cares! Just come for a couple of drinks. C'mon everyone would love to see you."

Well he is right, everyone *would* love to see me. I'm sold. "Alright, one drink, early, then I'm out!"

"Hell yeah! See you then."

"Heeeeyyy!!" The communal roar of the bar as I walk in the door is like Norm walking into Cheers except with 20 something southern drunk college kids rather than 40 something Boston alcoholics.

Out pops my buddy Ben, "What's up hero! Carry anyone down any steps lately? How's Oprah? Did she ask about me?"

"Yeah she called earlier, she was sorry she missed you."

"C'mon buddy let me buy you a drink"

"No way" Pee Wee the cute bartender says "this one's on me baby doll."

I guess being a pseudo American hero has it's privileges.

"Thank you darling, but you cut me off after this one. I have to make it a short night."

Pee Wee sticks out her bottom lip like a 5 year old, adding another uncomfortable similarity to a minor with her ribbon tied pig tails and knee high socks below her short plaid skirt. "Johnny, that makes me sad."

"I know sweetheart, there'll be other nights."

What a little tease.

Everyone's there and you know the drill with the guy that gets back in from out of town. No matter how hard you try, the 'just one drink' never works. It's almost as if there's a little imp that surfaces as soon as you make a declaration of responsible behavior. This imp sees this declaration as a challenge to derail this distorted idea of a low key evening and it usually wins. It does this with a combination of college girls in short skirts, the dark, easy on the eyes lighting of the bar (so your drunk eyes don't have to squint), and the message resonating in the back of your mind that says 'hey, you're only young once.' This message is, of course, louder than ever in light of recent events.

I look at my watch. "Oh shit!"

"It's 1:30! I have to get the hell out of here. Alright Josh, I really have to roll."

"Alright buddy, thanks for coming!"

I don't even say good bye, but just haul ass for the door. Goodbyes after a night like this can last another 15 minutes or depending on which girl is around, may not end at all. I head straight for the door but am stopped by my buddies Nick and Loftin.

"Hey man," Nick says, "you mind dropping us off at the house."

"Dude, I really have to.."

"C'mon, it'll take you like 10 extra minutes. It's not like you have to work tomorrow."

"Alright but hurry the hell up. I actually have shit to do tomorrow."

5 minutes later. . .

"What?!" I yell.

"I said 'Are you happy to be back?!'" Loftin yells at the top of his lungs, Kid Rock blasting in my Explorer.

"Yeah, I am!" I yell. "Boozing with you assholes sure beats the hell out of sitting on Osama's target."

Loftin laughs, "I hear you, buddy."

"Hey, which way do you want me to take you guys home." Loftin turns to Nick, "I dunno, just cut through Dan Allen Drive through campus."

"Sounds good."

I crank the wheel right off of Hillsborough Street and head down Dan Allen at about 45 miles an hour. A perfectly decent speed... unless you're in a 20 mph zone, which we just happen to be.

I'm a cowboy baby! We sing at the top of our lungs. *With the top let back and the sunshine....*

Blue Lights.

"Oh shit."

"Oh dude," Loftin says as he looks through the back window. "This is not good, are you alright to be driving?"

I turn down the radio as I look through the my side view mirror, "Goddamnit! Hell no I'm not alright, do you have any gum?"

"No, sorry dude. But I heard you could try sucking on a penny."

"What the?" Well I don't have a better idea. "Do you have one?"

"Yeah, here". He hands me the penny and I pop it in my mouth. What the hell is wrong with me? Idiot!

"Evening officer." Cue cheesy 'sober' smile which is made a little difficult with the penny in the side of my mouth.

"License and registration."

"Sure thing"

I fumble through my glove box and fish through McDonald's napkins, a map, a broken CD case and come out with what looks like a registration.

"That's not it son, it's right there." He points to my glove box. I grab the slip and give it to him.

"License?"

"Oh, right, sorry." I fumble through my wallet to find my license. Social Security card, gym membership, Visa, Oh great License. My nerves get the best of me and as my fat fingers attempt to form into a license retrieving claw I lose my coordination and flick my license at the officer's chest like I'm seven years old playing with baseball cards. Both the officer and I look down at the ground where the officer now has to bend to reach my license. I am so screwed.

"Sorry sir" I smile.

"Step out of the car son."

10 minutes later, I'm in the back of a squad car heading downtown. The same urban legend bullshit that made me stick a 'do you know where that thing's been' penny in my mouth has me in the back of the car inhaling and exhaling frantically in an effort to expend the alcohol breath that will inevitably be detected downtown. Man I am such a MORON!!

We pull into the parking deck downtown and the officer comes to my side of the car to let me out. He guides me out by my elbow like a handle, just like they do on COPS. Holy shit. Earlier today I was an American hero. Now, your average run of the mill criminal. We walk through a corridor to the booking area and then to the breathalyzer.

"Alright son, blow." The last time I ever want to hear that...in any context.

I lean down and give a breath that could have been better if I were a 90 year old asthmatic with emphysema.

"That's not gonna do son, c'mon stop messing around."

I bend back down, look over to the other breathalyzer and see my buddy Chad. I become immediately oblivious to my situation and think it appropriate to wave. Again, what the hell is wrong with me!? I might want to reconsider my life when I run into people I know at central booking.

I need new friends.

. . . maybe my friends need new friends.

I blow again

"Alright, come with me."

He doesn't let me go so I assume that the breathalyzer game didn't go my way. He leads me to a cell to sit for a while and brings me out to a lady that looks like Nel Carter to take my information.

Hurricanes & Firefighters

"Derek! What's up buddy?"

"Hey man. Nothing, just laying around watching TV."

"Cool. Well you have anything going on tonight?"

"Same old. Why?"

"Well, I know you're not big into hockey, but I've been invited to watch the Hurricane's opening game in the owner's suite tonight. They said that they'd do something for me on the ice during the Star Spangled Banner and I can bring a few people along."

"Dude. This 'hero' thing is getting hilarious."

"I know. You in?"

"Yeah, absolutely."

"Cool, I'm picking up Alice and Julie around 6:00 and we'll swing by and get you on the way."

"Hello John, I'm Maryann. I head up the PR for the team. Pleasure to meet you." She sticks out her hand. She is an attractive woman in her late thirties, whose formal demeanor and manor of professional dress make her seem older.

"Hi Maryanne. Great to meet you." I look around the owner's suite. "Thanks for having us."

"It's our pleasure. Please make your selves at home. The bar is over there and there is plenty of food. I'll come back and get you when we are ready for you to come down for the Star Spangled Banner."

Someone catches Maryann's eye behind me. She smiles and waves them over. Two guys in FDNY tee shirts walk over. One guy looks to be in his late thirties and is about 6'3" with blonde hair made darker by whatever he used to slick it back. The other guy is in his late twenties and stockier at a little under 6' with dark hair and darker skin.

"John," Maryann says as she put's her hand on the taller guy's shoulder, "This is Jimmy," she turns to the shorter guy, "and this is Nick. They've been kind enough to join us from New York. They are two of New York's finest firefighters. They were also down at Ground Zero that day. I'm sure you three have a lot to talk about. I'll see you all shortly," she holds up a clip board with a 'you know how it is' look, "I've got a thing with some sponsors." She heads out of the suite into the hall.

"*Marone*, I'll do a 'thing' to her, you know what I'm sayin'?" Nick elbows Jimmy who has an expression that looks like he's tasted something so good that it hurts.

54

"Yeah, I could get used to this 'southern bell' thing real quick. What do you think the chances are of me getting her to come back with me?"

"To Woodside? I don't know Jim. Something tells me that the closest she's been to Queens is having her daddy treat her like a Princess."

"I wasn't talking about forever, moron. I meant tonight."

Nick rolls his eyes, "Yeah, I thought she said that she couldn't wait for some whiskey soaked Mick to hit on her. I'm sure you're just her type."

Jimmy gives an 'oh really?' nod. "Oh and I guess she'd rather have a greasy guinea half her size?"

"Fuck you." Nick says.

"Fuck you, too."

So much for the pristine image of the 9/11 hero huh? At least I'm not the only one who can't change over night.

"Hey guys, I'm John Cerqueira."

They both look over as if I'd just appeared out of nowhere.

"Hey buddy," Nick shakes my hand, "how are things?"

"Good," I shake hands with Jimmy. "How you doing?"

"Good," Jimmy says, "so what are you a cop or you from a house in the city?"

Me? A cop? I'm not sure why that's funny other than that it's not true. Oh, and my mother would've beat my ass if I chose a job where I could be shot at every day. Who'd have thought that selling telecom in New York could've been more dangerous?

"No, actually, uh, my boss and I helped a woman in a wheelchair down from Tower 1…"

"No shit! You're that guy?" Jimmy says, "We heard about you. Nice job kid."

"Dude, I bet that was some scary shit." Nick says, "I mean, by the time we got down there, they just had us wait around outside, and that was fucking nuts. I can't imagine what it was like inside. We've been down there cleaning that mess up for months and it doesn't seem like we've made a dent. I can't imagine all that shit coming crashing down on me."

"It was pretty crazy. I'm just glad I got out and was able to get my ass back to North Carolina."

"Speaking of ass," Nick moves over to the window looking down at the arena and the ice. "This joint does have some high quality 'talent'. I mean, look at that!" He says as he bites his balled up fist like Lenny or Squiggy, one.

I look out the window as the girls of the Storm Squad, the 20 year olds that serve as hockey cheerleaders, come out on to the ice.

"Yeah," I say, "it's not bad for scenery." We walk back over to the bar and grab a beer.

"So you guys from Queens?"

"Born and raised," Jimmy takes a swig of beer. "Our house is out there too, we just came into the city that day 'cause they were calling everybody in the area."

"So did any of your guys have to go in?"

Both of the guys get straight faced. Jimmy shakes his head.

"No. None of our guys." He says without looking at me. "But we both knew some guys that, uh. . . We both knew some that did."

I understand the 'knew' and not 'know' to mean that whoever they knew that made it in the building, didn't make it out. I've not been in this situation yet. I've not met anyone else closer to the situation than I am. This is also the first time I've met anyone that lost anyone that they knew. Fortunately everyone in my office came out alive, and I didn't know anyone else in the building.

I worry what these guys think of me. Do they look down on me because I'm not a firefighter or a cop? Do they look at me as one of the people that were able to make it out because of the help from their buddies that weren't as lucky? Do they resent me for the notoriety I've received for doing nothing more than what they're expected to do every day?

I just want to tell them that I *don't* think I deserve it. That *they* are the real heroes. That I'm sorry for everyone they've lost and I think about them every day.

"Glad you made it out brother." Jimmy looks up from his beer and right into my eyes. Then, this big, crude, Irish guy from Woodside Queens looks away to Nick, misty. "I'm glad we're all here." He raises his beer. Nick and I do the same.

Jimmy walks over to the window again. We exist for a few seconds in an uncomfortable silence.

"Hey kid." He says without looking at me. His eyes fixed either on the ice or into space deep in thought. "Come here."

Oh no. I'm not sure if I'm prepared for any more of this heavy conversation. "Look, Jimmy I..." maybe if I apologize, I can nip this in the bud ant get the light mood back, "I...I didn't mean..."

"Let me ask you a question." He pauses. He's still not looking at me,

"You don't know that blonde in the cowboy hat down there do you?"

He turns to me with a 'dirty old man' grin. I guess he was tired of the heavy mood too.

I guess everybody finds their own way to deal with it all. For those of us that were downtown that day, what we saw... Some people lock them selves in their apartments, go see shrinks, and glue themselves to the news. Luckily there are also the others that do their best to regain the sense of normalcy we had on Monday the 10th. We get through it the best way we know how.

Me & Oprah

After *Good Morning America* I make a quick trip to the temporary office my company set up at 26th street, visit with my old co-workers for a while then head to the airport.

"My name is John Cerqueira I have a 12:20 flight to Raleigh-Durham."

The girl at the desk types the information on the computer and looks up at me confused. "Sir, you're not booked on a flight to RDU today."

Son of a...

"Sure I am. It was booked through ABC yesterday so maybe it is misplaced. Check again please."

She types the keyboard again and shakes her head. "I'm sorry sir, nothing. But maybe I can try looking another way."
She types some more, a little more, then still a little more. She stops and looks at me with the look of bad news. "Mr. Cerqueira, it appears that you are booked on a flight from Newark at 12:30 today, and this is LaGuardia."

Shit!!! Are you serious? Aww man. How the hell did I do that?

"How's that possible ma'am, I flew *in*to LaGuardia?"

Oh yeah, I was hoping to grab breakfast with my cousin in Jersey and requested to be sent out through Newark. I just didn't have enough time after the show. She stares back at me blankly.

"Well what happens now?"

"Sir, you'll have to buy another ticket."

"OK, how much?"

She types some more. Frowns. It's not looking good. "527 dollars...plus tax."

I storm away from the desk, pick up my phone and dial.

"ABC. This is Helen."

I explain to Helen the situation and she assures me she'll take care of getting me out through LaGuardia. She says she'll call me back in a few minutes. Whew, that was easy.

I'm getting hungry and begin looking for some fast food when my phone rings. Wow, that was fast huh?

The caller ID is a 312 number...Chicago.

"Hello, this is John."

"John."

It's Jay. He says my name in the same tone of a girlfriend calling to tell me that I'm 10 minutes late for dinner and the meatloaf is getting cold.

"Hey Jay, what's happening?"

"Oh, well I woke up and it was a beautiful morning…" he sounds like he's telling a fairytale, "I made myself some breakfast with a great big glass of orange juice and it looked like it was going to be a wonderful day," I'm sensing a 'but', he's not happy and wants to tell me that in the most melodramatic way possible. "And then I turn on the television and whom do I see on GMA but you, John Cerqueira. Hmm, funny?" He says 'hmm funny' so fast that I can tell he just couldn't wait to get to that part of the story.

"Oh yeah Jay, Good Morning America called and wanted me to be on the show. I know you didn't want me to do any other TV but I figured it wasn't a big deal since it's a multi-segment morning show, and such a different format from Oprah that…"

"Well you were wrong." He interrupts. Whoa, huffy! "It *is* a big deal. I'm just not sure what we're going to do now," he says in almost a threatening tone that starts to piss me off considering my last few weeks.

"Look Jay, *YOU* do what *YOU* want to. If you decide not to have me on the show, I got to tell you, I'm kind of okay with not flying while terrorists still want to fly planes into shit! You just tell me now brother, so I know if I'm heading up to Chicago or keeping my happy ass on the ground in safe Raleigh, North Carolina!"

"Whoa John, let's not get so worked up." Different tone now huh? "It won't result in anything like that. Can you just pretty please not do any other television? Pah-leeeeeeeze?"

"Whatever."

I hang up

"Welcome to Chicago Mr. Cerqueira, please let me take those for you." The chauffeur grabs my bags and those of my sister and mother who wouldn't pass up the chance for Oprah tickets and a free trip to Chicago.

"Thank you." I turn to my mom and sister. "Alright, this is us. Hop in!"

The four of us head off from the airport and I start reading through the Tribune and sipping a whiskey drink I made myself from the open bar in the limo like I'm Gordon Gecko. Hey, it's not everyday I'm escorted like some big shot.

I lean toward the driver so he sees me in the rear view mirror. "So I guess Oprah does things pretty top shelf, huh?" I raise my glass, which by the way I'm drinking at 1:00 in the afternoon.

"Oh yes sir. Ms. Winfrey takes exceptional care of her guests."

Why the hell does everyone everywhere in the country get to call her "Oprah" and everyone who works for her insists on calling her "Ms. Winfrey"?

"Evidently." I answer.

"I will tell you a secret if you promise not to tell."

Ooh, I love secrets.

"What's that?"

"This is the same limo used to pick up the guests for Jerry Springer. Except, they strip it of the liquor, the snacks, and the newspaper."

Snacks? Where are the snacks? I didn't see snacks.

"Wow! Really?"

"Oh yes sir. And rightfully so. I must say, there is a considerable difference between the caliber of guest on the Oprah show and the guests who appear on that other garbage."

Ooh I heard you say it, I heard you say "Op-rah" c'mon say it again. Don't be scared.

"Yeah I bet. I guess one day you're picking up Brad Pitt and the next day this limo has Geraldine from West Virginia bringing her boyfriend to the big city to tell him that their baby is really her step-brother's."

"You're more accurate than you think, sir."

"Well sorry to bring down the class average buddy. If you'd have had some Budweiser cans in here and a funnel, you might be confused as to which studio you were taking me to."

"At least you have a full set of teeth and something other than Hefty bags for luggage, sir."

"Well," I say in a thick country drawl, "I guess that makes me certifiable high class."

We get dropped off and I walk in the hotel lobby and see Mark and Dave from my office in New York. The CEO of our company flew the rest of the office out to Chicago to be in the studio audience. Either a really nice thing to do, or free advertising for the company on a nationally televised talk show. . . I'm deciding to err on the side of human kindness lately so I opt to assume the former.

"Johnny boy! Hurry up and drop your stuff upstairs. We're going to grab some drinks!"

It's about 2:00 in the afternoon, but hey, I have to spend this per diem somewhere, right?

We head up to a bar in Lincoln Park that seems like a pretty nice place. You know, low lighting, leather chairs, mahogany. We realize later that it's the kind of place that younger girls come to get picked up by rich older guys. Most of the office is there and we start to order appetizers from the cocktail waitress while 10 of us crowd around a small high table in the corner.

The semi-cute waitress, thin with shoulder length curly blonde hair comes up to the table. "So what's the occasion guys?" I grimace hoping this doesn't sound cheesy, "I know it sounds funny, but we're going to be on Oprah tomorrow."

"Oh wow! That's so great. What for? Has someone like, been abused or come from broken homes or something?" She laughs like she thinks she's clever.

"Actually, no. We uh, we were all from an office in the World Trade Center." I flash a smile trying not to look as wounded and crazy as I can tell she thinks I am.

"And these guys," Mark pipes in, pointing to Mike and me, "these two guys saved a lady in a wheelchair! They're fucking famous!!"

The waitress's eyes light up.

"Oh my God! That is so great! You guys are so sweet! I totally heard that story!" She raises her index finger like she has an idea and walks towards a guy who appears to be the manager. He follows her back to our table.

"Ladies and Gentlemen, my name is Rob. I'd like to offer you all our VIP section. Please follow me."

We follow him away from our cramped table passed a velvet roped section with deep couches and low lit lamps, on a platform raised about a foot or two from the rest of the cocktail area.

"You all, please enjoy your evening and rest assured that your entire bill is on the house." He turns to Mike and me. "Thank you for showing that there is good in this world."

I've waited tables before and realize that there's not a lot in the service industry that a customer gets without some type of ploy. I don't want to rain on anyone's parade, but half priced sushi is usually the close to, if not completely, spoiled fish bait from yesterday, the day before, or whenever it is that raw fish is no longer good to eat raw. And 'all you can eat' deals usually charge more than you would pay if you paid for all you really *could* eat. But this gesture seems genuine and we were all kind of touched by it.

This, along with the majority of us being out from under the cloud of depression in New York, raised our spirits, not to mention our level of alcohol consumption. The night ran on until a few of us ended up at some after hours club some random guy who claimed to be a club promoter told us about. It's one of those underground types of places without a sign, like in Swingers, that is supposed to make you cool just by knowing how to find it.

The place looks like an opium den (if those even exist anymore, if not, what I guess they used to look like). There is

Moroccan music playing, it's dim with low, red lights, and there are several covered booths for privacy everywhere.

I sit in a booth with an older guy from the office Ed, my buddy Matt, and Tiffany. Tiffany is a cute blonde from Long Island who I had a little crush on and had asked about my first week at the company. She had a boyfriend.

"So guys, how do you like this?" I grab and look at my drink then around to our booth. "A month ago we're working at the top of one of the tallest buildings in the world, and the next month we're getting smashed in Chicago about to be on national TV!"

"Well buddy, it's not like it's all fun and games. We dodged a pretty big bullet." Ed chimes in, "You and Mikey especially."

"It wasn't a bullet Eddie. It was a fucking 757! And we didn't "dodge" it." They look at me with their heads cocked like confused dogs. "The man upstairs was watching over us."

They all shake their heads. "You're damn right he was." Says Matt as he slams the rest of his drink down his throat. I'll say that none of us, even if we weren't in an opium den, would strike anyone as a group of regular church-goers.

Army Chaplain Major Juan Borges famously declared, "There are no atheists in foxholes." I guess tragedy in the face of danger *does* make us more spiritual. It's a good thing, in my opinion. I see it as a way for us to feel like someone or something is watching out for us, taking care of us, and hopefully guiding us. Also, maybe judging us and giving us some extrinsic motivation to do good while we're here suffering the mortal coil. I just hope that we can keep thinking and hopefully living with some type of purpose, or at least an appreciation for how precious all of this really is.

That night I hooked up with Tiff. Nothing big. Just the kind of middle-school, innocent, over-the-shirt, glad-to-be-alive affection. Don't worry, Tiff had broken up with her boyfriend. I have *some* morals.

The next morning marks my second nationally televised hangover. Mike and I arrive to the studio and are directed to a conference room, those sitting at the table being the guests and those standing around with clipboards clearly the producers of the show. The head, clip board holder is a thin black guy, in a snugly tailored suit that I can't identify as really nice or really cheap. Gotta be Jay.

"Okay so Lisa…are you here?" he asks

"Yes, I'm here." Says a pretty blonde, conservatively dressed, and noticeably pregnant, but in a cute, soccer mom, country club kind of way.

"Mike Benfante?"

"Present." Says Mike, yawning.

The clipboard holder in the cheap/expensive suit looks up at Mike, then at me. It's definitely Jay. He narrows his eyes and shifts his weight dramatically on his right leg so his hip juts out in pouting stance.

"So you must be John?" He says my name like he's just dropped an F-bomb. "Well I'm still not over our little tiff, but I guess we'll just have to deal with it now won't we?"

"I suppose so, Jay." I say smiling triumphantly like the sibling that got his way after going to his parents to settle a fight. I imagine that if he told Oprah about the situation, she told him to deal with it like an adult, which he is doing under much protest. Ha, Ha.

"Oh, by the way...I'm present for the record."

Jay glares at me and goes about his role call.

Next, Jay gives us the run down of how the show will work. Giuliani can't make it today due to attending several funerals in New York, so he will be on via satellite. Lisa will be on next, then Mike and I after that for the remainder of the show. Jay would like me to sit next to Oprah, who isn't here to greet us since she wants our conversation to be as candid as possible. I like the idea but did kind of want to hang out with Oprah. Turns out my dentist in North Carolina is Steadman's cousin and how cool would it be to play the name game, even if it's for a second with the most famous, powerful woman in showbiz. Not going to happen. So much for brunch with O.

"Okay everybody." Jay announces, "You all just hang out in the green room, watch the teleprompter and we'll come get you when your segment is up." He starts to walk out. "Everyone have a great show!" He says it like it's opening night on Broadway.

Mike and I hang out in the green room with Lisa, the cute pregnant blonde. She seems shy, and like she has a lot on her mind. Mike and I just make small talk quietly with one another while we watch the segment with Giuliani. Man that guy is awesome!

"Ok, Lisa, we're ready for you."

Lisa gets up with the speed of a woman with child.

"Good luck!" I say, for lack of a better idea of what to say in this situation. I wonder what her story is.

We turn to the teleprompter and the show comes back from the commercial break. Oprah begins to introduce her next guest. I begin to realize who Lisa is.

"...today we will meet the wife of Todd Beamer, one of the brave passengers on American Airlines flight 93 who battled with the terrorists who high jacked the fourth plane on that Tuesday morning. Of course while succeeding in stopping what would be another devastating attack, they themselves perished as the plane lost control and crashed into a field in Shanksville, Pennsylvania."

Mike and I look at one another in amazement. We don't say a word. We just watch the story, not believing the fact that this poor woman was sitting a few feet away from us minutes ago. If I had known I would have said something. But what? What do you say to someone that's gone through something like that? Guilt floods my heart and am reminded that while I've been goofing off, kissing the ground, and partying like the frat boy that I am. . . err, was, people are suffering and will continue to suffer from the loss of love ones.

Lisa tells the story of her husband calling her to tell her he loves her. Telling her that the plane is hijacked, and he and some other passengers are going to take on the terrorists. "I love you" then to the other would be heroes, "Alright guys...*let's roll*." This saying becomes an inspiration to the country and to our impending military campaign. The story is heavy and emotional. My mom tells me later that as soon as Oprah introduced Lisa Beamer, the entire studio audience reached under their chairs to grab the strategically placed boxes of tissue in preparation for what the producers rightfully judged to be a tear jerker. Mom says that sobs and sniffles were heard through the audience during the entire segment. Until...

> "And now the story of two brave men, Michael Benfante and John Cerqueira. Both worked on the 81st floor of Tower 1 of the World Trade Center. Mike had just finished a novel on the subway and had just arrived at the office, John was in the bathroom straightening his tie for a morning meeting. Both were unaware that they were to be stretched to their physical and emotional limits."

I stand in the wings, nervously tapping my foot, my hands trying to keep still in the pant pockets of the olive green suit and black tee-shirt ensemble I chose for my second national television appearance. Yes, it was a green suit with a tight black tee shirt. No, I am not in the NFL.

"Here they are…John Cerqueira and Mike Benfante."

The audience claps with a standing ovation. The applause lasts for what seems like forever. Mike and I walk up to the stage as I try to focus my eyes on the chair that will be mine. Just don't trip. Please just don't trip in front of millions of people. Oprah is on the stage and I am enthralled at how engaging she is without having said one word to me yet. She reaches out to shake my hand. "Thank you for coming," she says like I'm a guest in her home. "Please have a seat."

I sit down. The audience is still clapping and smiling, some are crying. My mother among them. The applause dies down. Oprah begins:

"So gentlemen. Working on the top of the world Trade center." People keep saying "the top" even though there were actually almost 30 floors above us. "The first plane hits and what happens?"

I'm sitting closest to Oprah so I begin. Still a little nervous but she has an innate talent for making me feel at ease. I stumble over the first few words and then I start to get my flow. It's like a normal conversation. Look at me go. . . Thank God I'm not going to come off like a tool with everyone watching, I mean, aside from the green suit.

I'm sorry, Camera Fright, this round goes to Mr. Cerqueira

We alternate between Mike and me talking. This is cool. Oprah Winfrey and me. Me and Oprah! Just hanging out like, well I don't know, just hanging out! She's so cool, so warm, so engaging that I forget I'm even on TV.

"…We'll be right back." I'm no producer but I guess this is the commercial break.

Immediately Oprah pops up out of her chair and heads for one of the crew.

"Bobby, we need to aim that light HERE." She points to somewhere on the stage speaking in a tone that is drastically different than 'sweet interview' Oprah. I guess this is 'business, I know what I'm doing' Oprah. "And how's my sound! Are these mic's coming through? I do NOT want a repeat of yesterday!" Wow! This lady is running the show! I get an image of my head of the cartoon graphic at the end of the show when the 'HARPO' block letters follow the caricature of Oprah and shoves her a little from behind. How far that is from the truth, huh? It is clear that nobody pushes this lady around. She continues to go through a checklist of lighting, sound, camera angles in a way that's not demeaning or bullying, just like a lady who is figuratively and quite literally running the show. A producer gives her the signal that there is 15 seconds until we're back on the air. She has a seat and we start to chat, still differently from the on the show Oprah, but like a real person. She even touches my foot. OK, I know I'm not exactly the show's target demographic, but I have to admit, I'm a little star struck. The producer gives us the old "Ed Sullivan silent finger countdown" three…two….

"Welcome back…" Oprah continues with the rest of the show with more follow up questions, comments from the audience, and we come to a pleasant close.

I still show the tape to dinner guests. My 15 minutes of fame actually lasts about 29 minutes…if you don't count commercials.

Julie Revisited

Well, if almost dying in a large scale terrorist attack at 22 years old doesn't kick you in the ass to take some chances, nothing will.

My parents came to pick me up from the city the Thursday after 9/11. We drove the 8 hours home, much of the time in complete silence. We arrived to the apartment that my parents were living in while their new house was getting built. Little did they know that the two bedroom would soon have to accommodate, one sister dropping out of college, another living at home during college near by, and their son who would be displaced by terrorists. We walked up the steps to the apartment, opened the door, and there she was. Tears in her eyes, arms wide, and coming toward me with a hug that took away my breath. We hug and I can feel her shaking with sobs and her hair against my face.

"I'm back." I say with a smile, like I just came back from the corner store.

"I'm so glad," she says "I've been sick." She squeezes her arms around my neck, my head is covered with her hair. It smells good. Safe.

I try to talk with muffled words , "Well you can stop now. I'm safe. We're all safe."

A few months after this scene and my reaping the physical benefits of the popularity with the ladies my 15 minutes has offered me, Julie and I ended up getting together on a trip down to Atlanta to watch NC State play Georgia Tech. We are in a bar, and get into a conversation about how much fun we have together. The next thing I know we are mugging down in the middle of the bar. All of our friends are around and they all applaud, presumably out of relief that the Mork and Mindy, Tony and Angela, Lois and Clark, Dawson and Joey, Ross and Rachel shenanigans of 4 years is over.

Our relationship takes off fast. 'I love you's' come instantly. It's a wonderful feeling to be loved and to love with everything you have. It's just, for a guy who's never felt like this and who's longest 'relationship' had lasted fewer than 2 months I have something in the back of my mind that says I might want to be a little cautious. Not of her, but of myself, of my goals, professional and otherwise telling me that this might not be the best time to try to drag someone else on my search for what's going to make me happy in life. Not only am I young but I'm in the middle of dealing with the biggest thing that's ever happened to me, life and death, to be or not to be, and every other existential question in the book.

But hey, Sartre be damned. These concerns are kept at bay and the next year is wonderful. It's refreshing to treat the girl who I always treated like a girlfriend actually as a girlfriend. We seem perfect for each other.

After the Impact

I look out the window. Fire and debris fall from above. 'Don't worry?' Don't fucking worry?! A plane, presumably a small commuter plane, has blasted into my office building and this guy tells me 'Don't worry'?!

"Well can I use the phone at least?"

The IT guy walks away and grabs a phone. I take this as a 'yes' and head to a mass of desks to find a working phone. The first phone I pick up works. I have to call my father.

A few weeks ago some idiot tried to parachute onto the Statue of Liberty's torch and got stuck. Despite my office's clear view of Ellis Island and the Statue of Liberty, the first I heard of it was from my buddy in Chicago who called me after seeing the story on the internet. If some schmuck dangling from the Statue of Liberty makes instant national news, I'm certain that a fire at the top of one of the tallest buildings in the world might get a little attention. I figure it would be a good idea to let the folks know I'm alright.

919-598…shit! I hang up. 919-598…damnit! I can't remember the number. One more time…919-598…

"Hey! Give that back!" I say as the guy that led me to the office grabs the phone out of my hand.

"Not now buddy. We got to get the hell out of here. Follow me toward the open stairwell."

I don't ask a question. This guy seems to know what's going on. I follow him along with the rest of the people in the room, toward the hallway.

Wait. Did he say 'stairwell'? Surely he doesn't intend for us to walk down 81 flights of stairs. It takes like 5 minutes to get up here in an elevator. How the hell long does it take to walk all the way to the…

A shoe.

One red high-heeled shoe catches my eye as it falls right outside the window. The shoe of some woman, maybe on the flight, maybe in the building. Lost in the hysteria maybe? Is she hurt? Dead?

Holy shit.

Stairs it is.

I follow the line of people through the hallway and to a stairwell. It's cold and bright and the smell of concrete and a chemical cleaner is overwhelming. It's the smell of a seldom occupied space. The line of people spread out. Any order within the group is abandoned and it seems like it's every man for himself. I clear the 81st to 68th flights in a matter of seconds, vaulting myself by the railings the same as I would in high school if I was late for class.

As I approach the 67th floor, I notice the flow of the stairwell slowing down. Before I can worry about what this traffic jam will mean in delaying my escape I see Mike, my branch manager.

"Mike!" I yell over the noise of the crowded stairwell. He can't hear me so I try again. He focuses his attention away from the stairs below and sees me.

"Johnny! Hey kid, you all right?"

Mike is in his late thirties, about six feet tall, athletic, with a receding head of curly brown hair and a Roman nose.

I run to join Mike on the landing.

"Mike, what the hell is going on? Where is everybody? How's the office?"

Mike is distracted as a stream of people pass us and he looks back up and down the stairs like he's looking for something.

"The office is completely fucked. They said some plane crashed into the floors above us. I got everybody out of the office and they're all on the way down below us."

"Great, well let's join them."

Mike is still looking up the stairs.

"Alright kid. You sure there aren't any of us from the office upstairs?"

I narrow my eyes to think. "No, not that I know of." Now let's get the hell out of here.

As we begin to head down the stairs, Mike in front of me, he stops and cocks his head like a dog hearing something almost inaudible from a distance.

"What? Mike, what are you doing?"

He moves past me up the stairs and stops on the landing.

"Do you hear that?"

I strain to listen.

"What? Mike what the hell are you talking about?"

"People. There are still people upstairs."

I focus again. I can hear them now, yelling down the hallway to one another. It's coming from the floors above us. Mike cups his hands around his mouth.

"Hey! This stairwell is open!" No answer, the people just keep yelling to each other. Mike tries again.

"Hey! Come down this way! Can you hear me!?"

Still nothing.

We stand there wondering what to do.

"Head on down the stairs, I'm going up." Mike says to me as he looks upstairs to the door, behind which are people that have no idea how to get out of here.

"Mike, I'm not letting you go back up by yourself. We don't even know how close this fire is."

"Well, you coming with me then?"

Shit, didn't we learn in Ms. Benucci's first grade class something about not going back upstairs in a fire, or jumping off a ship to save someone drowning? Don't they say that all that does is leave more people for the *real* rescuers to save? Oh well, I don't see Smokey the Bear or Ms Benucci here right now. . .

"Yeah, let's go."

Central Booking

"Name?"

"John Cerqueira"

"Date of birth?"

"May 3, 1979"

"Employer"

"Don't have an employer."

"Are you a student?"

"No ma'am, my job got blown up by terrorists." I'm slurring now I guess the shots right before I left the bar are catching up with me.

Nel stops writing and for the first time since I've been there, looks up from the form she's been filling out to make my criminal record official. Her eyes widen, her face made tight and stern from dealing with idiots, criminals, or both at 2:00 in the morning transforms into the same giddy look I would expect from her if she were picked as a contestant on the Price is Right. I can hear Rod Roddy as he would have said it, "Lateesha Johnson...Come on Dooowwwnnn!"

"Oh Lord!! You that boy from Oprah! Oh mah God!!" she turns to the officer who's looking around like he's in the middle of a Twilight Zone episode. "Why you got to arrest this boy, you know he been through enough already!" She turns back to me, "Baby, what's Oprah like? Is she pretty? Is she nice? Oooh, I bet she smells real nice too. I'm sorry you havin' such a bad night baby." She turns to someone behind her that I can't see. "Hey girl! Come out here and meet this boy that's been on Oprah. Oooh, he's cute too!"

I take back what I said before about liking attention. It's late, I'm drunk, I'm tired, and I'm in jail. I just want to go to bed.

I finally get my phone call.

"he..hello"
Oh shit she's definitely sleeping
"Jules, hey baby." I'm whispering
"John, what the hell are you doing? It's 3:00 in the morning."
"I know baby, I know. I'm...I'm in jail."
"Oh John." She sounds as if I call like this all the time. At the same time I can also hear sympathy in her voice. "I'll be there in 10 minutes."
"Thank you cutie. I'm so sorry."

20 minutes later Julie is there to pick me up

"So what do you think of your new convict boyfriend? Man baby, you hit the jackpot with this one. Unemployed, criminal record, *and* a torn psyche. How lucky are you?"

"Just get in the car, Rebel Without a Clue"

She kisses me

"You hungry."

"Actually no, just tired. Hey, do you mind taking me to my mom's office tomorrow to do that speaking thing?"

"What time?"

"Oh, in about 4 hours." I cringe and give my best cute/mischievous smile.

She groans, "Of course you little trouble maker."

"Is my life over now?" I ask her since she works for a law firm and is my most immediate source for legal information.

"No, it's just going to cost you a lot of money."

I wonder if talk show per diems can be used for attorney's fees. . .

We go home, get to bed, wake up in 4 hours and Jules takes me to Research Triangle Park. She sits in the car so no one realizes that she's come with me and that I can't drive. I head in to my mom's office and into the conference room to make her proud while reeking of alcohol and my mind wandering with how I'm getting out of this mess. Luckily no one notices, or seems to at least.

After hiring one attorney that I paid $700 just to screw up my limited privilege license, I decide I should shy away from the more discount legal services. This is no small charge against me and could really screw up my future, WTC hero or not. I give Julie a call at work.

"Hey sweetie, I think I might want to talk to one of your attorneys there for my little issue."

"Well John, my firm does civil, we don't really deal with criminal matters."

"I'm not a friggin' criminal Jules."

"I don't mean it like that, but technically for these purposes, you kind of are."

"Alright, whatever."

"OK look, I'll talk to one of our partners and see if she knows anyone."

"Thanks baby."

10 minutes later.

"John?"

"Yeah, hey what's up?"

"Great news, I just talked to Sara and she said the Big Guy will take your case."

The Big Guy knows everyone in town, is great friends with the D.A. and doubles as both one of the top criminal defense attorneys in Raleigh and as the Frat Boy Lawyer extraordinaire when it comes to drinking and minor 'dumb frat guy antic' types of charges. The catch is, he always comes with a hefty price tag usually paid by rich parents, a luxury my father made clear that I just don't have at this point.

"Baby, that's great," I say not all that enthusiastically, "but I can't afford him." I just picked up shifts waiting tables (can we say humility?) but am pretty sure tips aren't going to cover these fees.

"John, that's the best part. Sara thinks he'll do it for free!"

"Holy shit Jules! That's awesome! When can I meet him?"

"Tomorrow morning, just give his secretary a call."

"Oh thank you baby! You're the best!"

"I know, you can make it up to me later, trouble maker."

"Um, uh hi. I'm here to see the Big Guy."

I'm at the top of what seems to be a Crystal Palace in the middle of downtown, one of the more prestigious locations in Raleigh. The office seems coated with mahogany and marble. Classy digs indeed.

"Your name, Sugar?"

"John Cerqueira."

The receptionist gives me the same familiar smile that I've come to recognize over the last few months, the one that makes me realize she knows my tale.

"Of course, Mr. Cerqueira. The Big Guy is expecting you. Right this way."

She points me through a pair of double doors into a grand office coated with even more mahogany and with almost floor to ceiling panoramic views of Raleigh. And there sits the legend, the guy that could make a living if he were retained by NC State's

Greek community. Not an inch over 5 and a half feet, grey short cut hair, big moustache, and charisma seeping out of every pore.

"Hello Sir, I'm…"

"Mr. Cerqueira! How the hell are you son? Damn glad to meet you." He shakes my hand almost furiously and treats me like some high school football star that just won the state championship.

"Sir, I sure do appreciate you helping me out." I hand him a folder with what I consider to be the necessary information for my case. He takes the package and tosses it to the far end of the desk.

"You don't worry about that. You just let me take care of this so we can get this nasty mess out of your hair as soon as possible."

I'm shocked at the distinct difference between discount legal and this.. . well, this. I guess this is how it's done. Maybe it really is 'who you know.'

"I just thought you might need…"

"Buddy, I already have all I need to take care of this. You actually didn't really even have to come down here today, but I sure did want to meet you and I'm glad to help you in any way I can."

This guy rocks! We shoot the breeze for a while and he gives me the run down of trial dates, how we'll probably ask for a continuance until we get a judge that he thinks could be most sympathetic. We continue the case three times. The fourth time I get a call.

"John?"

"Yes?"

"Hey darlin', this is Dianne, the Big Guy's assistant."

"Oh hey, Dianne! What's going on?"

"John, the Big Guy wanted me to let you know that tomorrow we are going to proceed with the trial. We think that this judge will be…well, a little more lenient."

I start to sweat and don't answer.

"Don't worry honey, you'll be fine. Just look your best and he'll will take care of everything."

The next day is just like a full trial, except without the jury. Oh yeah, with one difference: Before the trial the judge asks me to approach the bench, quite an intimidating request to grant but hey, who's the judge, right? I approach the bench sheepishly, "Um yes your honor?"

What happens next still dumbfounds me. The judge actually stands up out of his chair, leans over, and extends his hand. "Son, I just wanted to shake your hand. I want you to know that all of us here are real proud of you."

Seriously? You have got to be kidding me. That has to be a good sign, right?

I sit back down and the trial begins. The A.D.A gives the facts of the case. The facts are that I had a BAC level over the legal limit while operating a vehicle. The Big Guy's response to that is, more or less, "Yes, these facts are strong and true, but we know that the verdict is always up to your honor's discretion." The judge says something that I would be able to hear if my telltale heart wasn't pumping blood so fast through my body that I am temporarily rendered deaf, and just as my hearing comes back I hear, "On the count of driving while intoxicated, I find the defendant......

"Not Guilty."

I'm speechless, and I grab on the table in front of me in case I pass out from the adrenaline shot. I just stand there with my mouth wide open. The Big Guy leans over to me and whispers, "Don't say a word. Get the hell out of here. I'll meet you in the hall in a minute." I do as he says and head out into the hall with the knowledge that I have just dodged my second bullet in under a year. Holy shit that is huge. No more stupid shit. My free hero pass has officially been punched. The Big Guy comes out in no time.

"Sir, thank you so much! I don't know how to thank you. If I can do anything, anything at all. . ."

"Just keep out of trouble and hope we don't run into each other anymore."

"Will do, and…"

His cell phone rings. "I have to take this"

As he walks away a man in a dirty tee shirt, unkempt dread locks and bloodshot eyes bursts out of the courtroom, looks both ways until he sees the Big Guy and heads for him. "Hey man! Hey, I got to talk to you! How much you cost?! Hey!!"

Flip a Coin. . .

"John, good morning, this is Laney from the Wolfpack Club here at NC State," says a chipper voice with an Eastern North Carolina accent coming out of the receiver.

"Good morning Laney. What can I do for you?" I say politely.

"Well, I'm not sure if you were planning to come to the State/ Carolina game next weekend, but we'd like to invite you to come watch it in the field house with our other distinguished alumni, and to be honored on the field at half time."

Wow, other 'distinguished' alumni. Kind of has a nice ring to it.

"Well, that sounds great Laney. Thank you so much for the invitation. I would love to join you guys."

"Wonderful! Well, we have four passes for you and whomever you'd like to bring, and there will be a continental breakfast served in the field house around 10:00."

"Sounds great. I'll see you there."

The next Saturday morning I drive over to Carter Finley Stadium. I stop at the usual tailgate spot to meet up with everybody. I down some Bojangles Biscuits, some sweet tea, and hashbrowns, glad-hand everyone, and head up to the Field House. Hey, there's a classy way to go to a football game, then there's our way... I'm not opposed to the former, but a college football game in the south isn't complete without a biscuit and fried chicken.

Upon entering the Field House it looks like a scene from Caddyshack. Mostly older, seemingly wealthy donors, in cardigans with collared shirts. The women are all dressed conservatively in below the knee skirts, sweaters, and pearls. I walk in, stop, and try to get my bearings for where I should go next, since I don't recognize a soul. I've already had a couple of shots at the tailgate (oh, yeah, forgot to mention bourbon in that little chicken & biscuits combo) and I wasn't ready to hang out with grown-ups just yet. A girl who seems to recognize me comes out from the crowd. She has a plain but pleasant face, cute athletic body, and perfectly coiffed shoulder length blonde hair. She walks toward me, smiling.

"You must be John! I recognize you from television."

I reach out to shake her hand., "Laney? It's a pleasure."

"Likewise," she's looking at me like a damn celebrity. "Please follow me. There are several people I'd like you to meet." I follow her bouncing curls as the saunters through the crowd like she's done it a million times this morning. I'm still a little concerned about bumping into one of these people and causing a spilled mimosa disaster. We finally stop, tragedy avoided.

"John Cerqueira, I would like you to meet our chancellor, Mary Ann Fox."

"It's a pleasure to meet you John. We are so proud of you."

"Thank you ma'am. It's a pleasure to meet you as well."

"So I bet you're happy to be back at home huh?"

"Yes ma'am, and I have to say," I look around to our surroundings, "this is certainly a nice way to come back."

"Well please enjoy the game and get your fill of some of this delicious food."

"I sure will. Wonderful meeting you."

"Ooh, John follow me." Laney grabs my arm and we move through the crowd again, towards a distinguished looking man with white hair.

"Governor Easley, I'd like you to meet John Cerqueira. John this is Governor Mike Easley." Now of course I knew the name, I just didn't know what this guy looked like.

"John, it is an absolute honor to meet you." He turns to a tall, slender, pretty woman of about 45 years old next to him. "This is the brave young man I was telling you about. The one from the World Trade Center."

The woman's eyes scan me from head to toe. "Well Mike, you never mentioned that he was this handsome."

I actually blush.

"Well it's not every day you find someone like us with the whole package." The Governor winks at me when he says this.

"Thank you ma'am, I'm John Cerqueira, pleasure to meet you."

The woman reaches out her hand, "The pleasure is all mine."

"John?" I turn to see whose voice that is. "John Cerqueira?" I turn and see my friend Tracy trying to navigate a sitting area to get to me. Tracy has dark curly hair, sharp facial features and is a thin girl with the same figure as she had as a high school cross country runner. She and I went to high school together and we dated briefly her freshman year, my sophomore year in college. Her Dad was an assistant Dean at State for a while. "John! It is so good to see you! I've heard about everything and I'm so glad you're okay."

She gives me a hug.

"Thank you darlin'. What have you been up to?"

"Oh just finishing school and applying to law school for next year."

"That's awesome. Good for you."

"You know who would love to see you?" Clearly a rhetorical question, "My Dad!" She grabs my hand and again I find myself being led through the crowd. "Daddy! You remember John Cerqueira right?"

Her dad is a kind, academic looking man with glasses, and a sweater vest. "Of course I do. So good to see you John." He shakes my hand vigorously and slaps me on the back. "Tracy told me you were in those Towers before this whole hero business, even

94

before the news made its way down to us. Son we were so worried about you and sure are glad you've made it out."

"Thank you, sir. It's great seeing you again."

"Hey John," Tracy's dad turns to a tall man next to him with a boyish face, but also the presence of possibly one of the most important people in the room. "John, this is one of our nation's finest Senators, John Edwards." I had heard the name before, and I think I even voted for him...

"Well you are too kind," Senator Edwards says to Tracy's dad. "Delighted to meet you, John. I heard that President Bush mentioned you in the address at the National Cathedral, but it wasn't until just recently that I realized that you're from right here in Raleigh."

"Yes sir, grown up around here since I was 7."

"Well son, you've been the buzz in this room all morning."

"Well thank you."

"And I guess we'll be enjoying each other's company during half time and the coin toss."

The coin toss?

"OK, we're ready for you." Laney says to Senator Edwards and I as she is followed by the Governor and the Chancellor. "Try to toss it in our favor, John." She smiles.

The five of us are led to the sidelines and I can hear the announcer introducing us. The chancellor, the governor, then Senator Edwards... all are met with a polite and steady round of applause.

"And now, one of our own, recent Wolfpack alumni, was working on the 81st floor of the World Trade Center, and on that terrible day in our nation's history, found it within himself to not only escape with only minutes to spare, but also to, with the help of his boss, carry a disabled woman to safety. We honor this man as one of our own, and a true American Hero...John Cerqueira."

The echo I expected from the PA is drowned out by the eruption of applause and cheers of more than 50,000 people. I'm startled, physically startled by the noise, then emotionally startled by the response. What is going on here? It's just me. All of this over ME? I don't know how to respond to this. Do I wave? Do I smile? Do a do a friggin' back flip. Nobody ever prepares you for something like this. My default reaction is to do nothing. I stand in front of 50,000 people who for now, are my cheering fans, and stand stiff as a board and straight faced as a general. I flip the coin and grimace as UNC wins the toss. Whoops.

I lighten up a little later when Governor Easley and Senator Edwards present me with an award at half time. It is the Order of the Long Leaf Pine which is, evidently, the highest honor a civilian in North Carolina can receive. This time I actually smile when the second roar from the crowd comes. Again, I'm amazed that all of this effort, attention, this commotion, is all just over me.

Do these people know who I am? Do they know that I'm not a hero, I'm just a guy who isn't cold hearted enough to leave a wheelchair bound woman in a burning building? I mean, who, except some sick bastard who drowns puppies in rubbing alcohol, wouldn't do that? Do they know that I binge drink, do donuts in empty parking lots with my friends? Do they know I sometimes throw tantrums like a spoiled child when I don't get my way? If they did, would they still like me? How am I going to keep who I am a secret so that these people, so that everyone isn't disappointed in me?

This guilt rears its head every time I'm in a similar situation until it makes these events and honors not even fun anymore.

This feeling is not easy to shake. Call it survivor's guilt or some other type of guilt, but it sticks with me.

Months later I emerge from the limo that picked me up from my hotel in midtown Manhattan. I walk into the Waldorf Astoria Hotel and passed a sign leading to a ballroom reserved for the *Christopher Reeve Paralysis Foundation.* Photographers are snapping pictures, celebrities are everywhere, and the usher leads the other guests and I to our tables. All of these people, the who's who of Manhattan philanthropy, and those stricken by paralysis are here to honor "Superman" and to help him fight the battle to let him and other's like him lead a better life.

The night is wonderful, the food terrific, David Blaine performs one his magic acts. The lovely Dana Reeves works the hundreds of tables with the grace of a queen. And then Helen Hunt approaches the podium, the crowd goes silent...

"We here at the Christopher Reeve Paralysis foundation are thrilled at the progress we are making to find a way to repair the nerve damage that leaves countless members of the world dealing with the challenges of paralysis. It is your donations that fund the work of an army of scientists that are, everyday, getting closer to making the dream to let people like Chris walk again, a reality."

The crowd applauds.

"I would also like to take this opportunity to thank two very special men."

What the hell is this now?

"These men embody what the foundation is all about. Literally lending a helping hand to one of our fellow human beings who is faced with a challenge that is all too familiar to the people in this room. These men risked their lives in the face of evil on September 11, 2001, to rescue a wheelchair bound woman. Down sixty-eight flights of stairs these men carried Tina Hansen to bring her to safety just minutes before their tower's collapse. Michael Benfante and John Cerqueira, please stand up gentlemen." We stand up and the applause begins. "Ladies and gentlemen, these men are the true manifestation of the spirit that brings us all here tonight."

The applause begins to gain momentum. I take in the scene as best as I can until I'm blinded by the spotlight.

My humility, or more appropriately my guilt for not being the person that they think I am, creates a crushing sense of embarrassment.

It is all a lie!

I am not a hero!

98

I've never lived like a hero and I sure as hell don't now!

Now don't get me wrong, I am flattered. Flattered by the honors, flattered by the rewards, flattered by the kind words from politicians, celebrities, reporters, religious figures, but the kind words are so much pressure. I begin to hate this label of 'hero' not so much for what it stands for, but because for everything I am, and for everything that I am not, it doesn't apply to me, no matter how I've somehow fooled everyone to think otherwise.

I, by no choice of my own, have had my name uttered in the same breath as war heroes, members of public safety, members of not for profit organizations, and those who adapt their lives every single day to live with debilitating disease and loss of mobility, not to mention their families. There is no way I deserve to be considered even the least bit similar to these people. When everyone finds out who I am, what I am, they will know that I can't possibly be compared to those that truly *have earned* the right to be an inspiration to others, to truly be called a 'hero.'

I want to scream out to everyone and tell them every bad thing I have ever done.

"I drink! I smoke! I have sex! I cut people off in traffic! I curse like a sailor! I take the Lord's name in vain! I'm selfish! I was a spoiled teenager who made my parents' lives a living hell! I tell politically incorrect jokes!"

"And if I had known that the building was going to collapse and that I'd barely make it out….how do you know that I wouldn't have left that lady there! YOU DON"T KNOW! I DON'T EVEN KNOW! I'LL NEVER KNOW!!! STOP CALLING ME A HERO!!!"

Of course I don't say any off this. Not now, not really ever. But whenever I'm referred to as a hero… it hurts just a little bit to realize how far that really is from the truth.

Looking back

I'm typing on my computer at my desk in the middle of Windows on the World. There is nothing else around me. I'm all alone.

I look up, feel heat getting closer. A comet is coming right for me. I have no time to move and it crashes in an explosion into my desk. I look around and the room is now filled with people. Some are banging on the windows, some are sitting at their desks, others are standing in place. They are all on fire.

"Everybody get the hell out!!" I try to scream at the top of my lungs, but no words come out.

"Help us! Please John, help us!" The voices of the others in the room say, but now nobody is moving. They all continue to burn. They look like mannequins standing completely still, burning, just burning until their skin turns to ash.

I run out of the room grabbing as many pieces of mannequins as I can.

"John, please help us! It's so hot! It hurts! Please. Please. Please. . ."

I run to the window to get out. A man in a suit is sitting next to me on a window sill. He looks at me, smiles, and leans back like a SCUBA diver off the side of a boat. His body rocks back until he falls out of the window.

I jump out of the window after him, but the fall is no longer than jumping from a flight of stairs. I reach the ground and run as fast as I can run over a bridge far away from the city until I can't make anything out but a silhouette of buildings. I am alone on an island in the middle of the water with a clear view of the city.

The tallest building begins to shake. The buildings closest to it shake as well. A chain reaction, like a shock wave, moves throughout the entire city. Then, one after another the buildings begin to collapse.

"Help us John! We can't breathe! Come back for us! My family is worried!"

I hold my hand in front of my face, it begins to melt. My flesh falls off of me like a marshmallow over a campfire.

I'm startled awake by my own gasp. I'm flat on my back in my bed. I sit up. Sweat is dripping down my neck in pools and my hair is soaked. I'm breathing fast. The perspiration that outlines me is almost twice the size of my body.

I can look forward to this scene once every couple of months.

Running to Stand Still

"I have to get out of here," I say as Julie and I sit on the balcony of her Raleigh apartment.

"What do you mean?" She's worried.

"Jules, I don't know, I'm just not happy here. Not happy with my life. I feel like I've given up, just being back in the place I'm from so soon."

She looks offended and sad. "You're unhappy with me?"

"No baby, not with *you*. With *ME*!" I look off the balcony onto the quiet street below. "I was so happy in New York. I felt like I was *doing* something with my life, hell at least something different, then one little bump in the road and I give it up?" I get up and Julie grabs me to sit back down.

"John, that wasn't a BUMP IN THE ROAD a year ago, three thousand people were murdered and you were almost one of them. You deserve a rest from all of that."

What? No I don't, you never deserve to abandon what's important to you even if what's important to you is just the *search* for what's important.

"No. No I don't, I have to find something, I have to find somewhere."

Moving to Atlanta

I knock on the door of the home office in Papermill Office Park, suburban Marietta Georgia. I signed the lease for my place in midtown Atlanta over the weekend and just got off the phone with Julie, still sobbing about how we were going to make a long distance relationship work. I assured her that we would make it through but that I had to go so I could be ready for my first day at Aslan Training.

Knock, knock. "Hello! Hello, is anyone here?"

The front reception office is empty and Tom pops out with his cup of coffee. He's dressed in jeans, a button-up and loafers. I guess you can do whatever you want when you own the company. Right behind me Tab, Tom's partner pops in.

"Tommy!!"

Tab has been traveling on a training trip and hasn't been home or in the office in about a week. They shake hands and hug like they're old friends. Not co-workers, but people that are really happy to see each other. I could get used to this place.

"Hey Tab, this is Johnny Cerqueira, the guy I was telling you about."

"Welcome, buddy. So Tom didn't scare you off yet, huh?"

"Well I just walked in so the day is still early yet."

"Well make yourself at home and let me know if you need anything."

Tab heads over to the break room and pours a cup of coffee, heads to his office, singing presumably the tune that was on the radio on his way in this morning. This guy seriously seems like the happiest person I've met in a long time.

The longer I work at this small consulting company, the more I realize that this isn't an act. In fact, both Tom and Tab seemed to have this secret formula that keeps them in a good mood. They have everything. A lucrative business that they enjoy, great families, wives, kids that they spend plenty of time with, great friends, and they all seem very spiritual, and not afraid to talk about it at work. The both of them, and their wives, come from affluent Buckhead families but decided to forgo the high society lifestyles for life in the still very nice but not nearly as pretentious, Marietta.

Tom tells me that he just didn't want his kids growing up in a keeping with the Jones's environment. He cites several examples of friends of his who never see their kids and live empty lives spending way too much time figuring out how to spend their money. Unexpectedly, Tom's humble approach to life affects me as well. Tom and I talk a lot on our business trips about this and just about everything else. Tom is a youth group leader at his church and is great at engaging in conversation that makes you feel like he really cares about you, mainly because he actually does.

He is also moral, and refreshingly non-judgmental, which puts me more at ease than I would expect with a self-proclaimed Fundamentalist Christian. We talk about my family, girlfriends, our past, both good and bad, and of course 9/11. It doesn't bother me to talk about this at all with Tom since he is really sincere and interested in what I went through, and more so about how it's changed me. Tom's interest forces me to think more about how I've changed and I begin to realize that not only do I want to have more fun now, since you never know when your time is up, but I also find that I make more of an effort to have a great relationship with my folks, even if it is from 400 miles away. During the year I work at Aslan, Tom and I develop a friendship similar to a father-son bond as I'm the youngest person in the office and the person that travels the most with him.

The sales training program taught by Aslan is not your typical workshop on hard nosed sales techniques. It's more about going into a sale with no other motive than doing what is best for the customer. They call it 'Other Centered Selling' based on the principle that if all you do is help people then you'll eventually help yourself. Tom says that he knew when he met me that he would hire me but I can't reconcile that with how much of a hard sales guy I was and how that might not work with this theory.

"Your energy", Tom says, "I can teach you to tone down and refine your skills, but the energy of a sales guy is inherent. You're born with or without it, and you my friend, were born with it."

Even though the job environment and the guys are great, I start to grow weary of the work. The trips to clients are great but they are few and far between. I mostly sit in an office with a little window calling on Sales Directors and VP's to drum up interest in our training program and have them pay for our trip to their offices to assess their company and tell them how we might be able to help. This kind of proposition is pretty difficult in the unstable economy post 9/11, when companies were just happy to survive. This makes selling telecom in the city, the job I had in Tower One, seem like a cake walk. Not only is it harder to get these higher level clients on the phone, but the much higher price of our consulting that isn't included in their budget makes it even more difficult to get an executive on board when they pick up the phone during their busy day. Despite the difficulty Tom is thrilled at my success…I disagree.

I grow tired of Atlanta too. Not that it's a bad place, it's just not New York. But hey, there's only one. The first time I realize just how different Atlanta is when I'm looking for apartments and just can't find anything I like. Everything looks the same, it's not new enough to be really nice but not old enough to have the character of many of the Manhattan neighborhoods. On one stop of my apartment search the leasing agent, who reminds me of a cast member from Designing Women, can see that I'm not impressed.

"Honey, you just don't seem excited about our property."

"No, I guess you're right."

"Well in that case I'd be happy to help you find something you like, even if you don't live here. What type of place are you looking for?"

"Well I most recently lived in New York, and it seems like everything up there is older, like turn of the century, or older, and it all seems to have a lot more character. Where is Atlanta's 'old part?'"

She looks at me with a smile that seems both contemptuous and sympathetic at the same time. It almost says 'Oh bless your heart you little yankee bastard, how clueless you are'.

"Oh, well Sugar, if you know your history, you should know y'all burned all that."

Of course she is referring to 'The War of Northern Aggression' for which her 'y'all' is a little misguided since neither I nor any member of my family had even immigrated to the States by that time, no less did they serve in the Union Army. Despite this little tidbit, I don't take the time correct her, not having the energy to engage in the North versus South battle that I've been so well versed in since my family moved to North Carolina from Jersey when I was seven.

I just smile back, thank her for her help and walk out of the leasing office with the undeniable truth that I just can't replace the good old Big Apple with the 'New York of the South' no matter how hard I may try.

Julie considered going to law school around Atlanta but instead chose to go to Wake Forest.

"John, I want to practice in North Carolina. This is a better move for me. Besides, we wouldn't see each other a lot anyway during my first year with the workload."

Even though Wake Forest is only two hours from Raleigh, law school anywhere is worlds apart from what she's used to. She notices this after her first happy hour sponsored by the school.

"Hey sweetheart, how was your thing?" I'm on my cell phone at a Waffle House after bars in Atlanta.

"It was okay, I guess."

"What's wrong?" I say with a mouthful of eggs and hash browns.

"Nothing, it's just that it's going to be a lot different."

"Different from what?" I point to the waitress to refill my coffee.

"From people we hang out with. It seems like everyone here is so pretentious."

"Oh baby, you can be just as pretentious as the rest of them, you'll see."

"Very funny. No, it's just, for example, this one kid, drunk out of his mind, comes up to me and is trying to make conversation but can barely speak. And when I asked him what he said, his response was 'Do you know who my family is?' I guess he was insulted that I didn't know who they were, but who the hell says that?!"

"Well did you find out who they were?" I like to make jokes to lighten the mood when there is little else I can do.

"It doesn't matter. I just miss you."

"I miss you too, baby doll," I really do, "maybe my next city can be Charlotte after Atlanta. I've always liked Charlotte."

"I just can't wait until we are able to be together again."

"Me too, sweetheart."

I really do mean it. It's just that I'm not that close to getting back to North Carolina yet.

Day after, cigarettes

My eyes are burning red. My throat is sore from coughing. I can still taste and smell yesterday. Yesterday is still lodged in my nostrils and throat. The smell is wafting through the city, even up to 91st street.

Aside from that it's a clear, relatively cool day, beautiful any other day. It'll be a lot better if I can grab a pack of cigarettes from the corner. I walk down the block into the bodega, "I'll take a pack of Parliaments." I hand the Arab clerk my credit card, I come here often and this is the drill. He looks at me with a scared look that says he has news that will not make me happy. I look to his right on the wall a sign written in red ink 'credit card not working'. I turn to walk to the back of the store where the ATM is. The clerk says nothing but before I get to the machine, I see a sign taped to the ATM written on notebook paper 'ATM not working'.

"GODDAMNITT!!!!" I scream. "MOTHER FUCKER!!!" I start to beat the machine punching it with the heel of my hand in the old kung fu nose-through-the-brain move. I continue to scream, some words and some just primal noises and beat the machine until my hand hurts. The machine appears unphased and remains defiant with the unchanged message that money's not coming out of this thing today. I gain the best sense of composure I can by taking a deep breath (interrupted by a violent series of Doc Holliday-esque coughs).

I look down, pause, then turn to walk toward the clerk behind the counter. I move slowly, deliberately, shove my hand into my right pocket and pull out the only two dollars I have. Calmly, but intensely, like a man ready to snap...again. I stare at the clerk with an unintentional but distinctly threatening manor. He is usually the first person I see in the morning, but today he has the pleasure of being the first person to piss me off by doing nothing else but representing the inconvenience of this city, this city that two days ago I found endearing but now detest.

"I have two dollars", I grab his hand and put the money in it, close his hand and squeeze hard. He looks more scared but doesn't do anything at all (in retrospect probably paralyzed by reports of Arab bashing). "I want...*cough, cough,* a pack...*cough, cough* of Parliament lights.*" He looks at me not at the case of cigarettes above the counter, raises his hand above his head and comes down with two packs. "Thank you" I say, "have a nice day."

He says nothing, just stares into my red bloodshot eyes, not scared now, but almost curious and concerned. I answer his stare with a dominant gaze, grab a lighter off the counter, light my cigarette and walk out towards my apartment. My cousin Anthony is on his way from Jersey to get me out of this hell hole.

Seattle with Skip

I started at Aslan Training and Development during an exciting time in the company. They've just landed their largest contract since the company's inception with the help of their new partner Skip. Skip is an ex-global VP for Oracle who, balding and about 5 and a half feet tall, he is their sales guy extraordinaire. He's basically a little guy with a big mouth that has made him a *lot* of money. He's one of those extreme sports, mid life crisis guys with whom we at Aslan have the pleasure of making the acquaintance on the down slope of his career. He's at a point when he wants to enjoy his money, reconnect with his teenage kids, and have fun. This job is basically his retirement.

To get me familiar with Aslan's training program, Tom decides to send me to Seattle with Skip for a client visit. The trip is enlightening professionally but most notable is our conversation after a dinner of Seattle's best steak and wine that Skip could find. This is a man that spares no expense.

"So John," Skip leans in over the table with a look that seems like he wants to make me uncomfortable, "tell me about yourself".

"Well", I start "I'm originally from…"

"Not that part, you know what I mean."

"Oh, the Trade Center stuff?"

"Yeah, the Trade Center stuff." Skip smiles, satisfied that he's getting what he wants. I can rehash this same story like a have a hundred times in my sleep so I start.

"I worked for a company called Network Plus. I got into work late that…"

"Yeah, I read the USA Today article, too." He takes a sip of wine and looks down into the glass. "I don't want the story, I want to know how the story affects YOU."

"Oh, in that case. I like to spend a lot more time with my family, try not to take anything for granted, you know stuff like that."

"Understood. What do you remember most about the day?"

"Well, mostly the smells, the sounds, the fear."

"The fear?"

"Yeah, the fear"

"Were you scared, really?"

Who the hell does this guy think he is?

"Hell yeah I was scared, there were Goddamn terrorists trying to kill me and 50,000 other people. Anybody would be scared."

Skip can see he's insulted me but seems to get a kick out of it as if he's planned it and enjoys my response. "You're right, most people would. But I'll ask again… were *you*?"

I hesitate, sigh, look away.

"I… well… " I reconsider my words then proceed. "Can I tell you something that I've not told anybody else?"

"Have at it."

"Looking back I don't remember being scared. When I look back I… " I pause.

"You what?" He looks at me waiting for what he seems to know is coming.

"When I look back I see it almost like an…an adventure or like a challenge I was able to overcome."

He smiles big, takes another sip of wine, and sits back in his chair. "I knew it."

"I didn't mean it like that," I blurt out, wanting nothing more than to take that last comment back. How insensitive and demented can I be to look at one of the most tragic events in our nation's history and think it's my own little Indiana Jones adventure? I am such a bastard.

"It's okay John."

"No it's not. I didn't mean it. I mean, people died, families were torn apart, the confidence of the city and the nation shattered and I sit here and think of it as some type of game. What the hell is wrong with me?"

Skip looks serious now, like a father ready to reprimand a child. He puts down his wine glass and leans forward and stares at me intensely.

"John, you were in the middle of the most catastrophic event of our lifetime. Not only did you escape within minutes of your life, but the good Lord used you and your boss to deliver another human being to safety. While of course a tragic day, it was also the day that you proved to yourself that you are a survivor, that you have what it takes to be in the face of the most evil shit on this earth and through will power and the Grace of God, persevere."

Skip's face lightens up again, "Son, I'd be disappointed if you *didn't* think of that as an adventure. We get so hung up on being politically correct that we deny what is a natural tendency for a guy to live for and thrive off of challenge. From the first day I met you, you've not stuck me as someone emotionally wounded. You carry yourself with a confidence just short of a swagger that says that you are capable to handle anything thrown at you. So don't you dare apologize for thinking of 9/11 as your adventure. Few of us ever have the chance to test ourselves in such a way. You have and you've passed with flying colors. That's what makes you, *you*. And for that, my friend," he raises his glass in a toast, "I applaud you."

An Unexpected Traveling Companion

I look to the wall and walk over to the fire extinguisher, break the glass case, pull it off the wall and run up the stairs with Mike. We pull open the heavy steel door and run into the hallway. We see the backs of two men and a woman, all in suits, running the other way.

"Hey!" They turn around when they hear my voice. "This stairwell is open. Get down, quick!" The three people run towards me. I follow them with my eyes as they run through the door and down the stairs. When I look up Mike is gone. I yell for him.

"Over here!" I hear him from around the corner and follow his voice. I see him banging on glass doors, which lead to an office, trying without much luck to get the attention of a group of people standing frozen with their backs to us. I run up to meet him and join him banging on the glass. Finally a 30 something man in a suit breaks away from the group, runs to the door, and lets us in. Mike and I push pass him into the office.

"Hey! Everybody get the hell out of here!" I yell, in what I notice to be quite the contrasting tone than is usually used in an office.

"Let's go everybody," some people turn their heads, but not their bodies, to look at Mike as he says, "the building is on fire and there is an open stairwell right around the corner."

No one moves. Not at all. I get frustrated and walk up to the group and grab a blonde woman in a blue skirt suit by the shoulders.

"Hey lady! Did you hear what we said!" I say as I pull her backwards. She doesn't protest but doesn't move with me freely either and as she moves out of the way, I see what this group of people has been so focused on that they were paying us no attention.

In the middle of a semicircle formed by non-descript white collar office workers sits a small blonde woman of about 40. If she were standing she would be less than 5 feet tall and doesn't look to be any more than 100 pounds. She looks up at us like a child. As soon as I am able to break away from her striking gaze I notice why our efforts begging everyone to run down the stairs have been, so far, unsuccessful. I notice the control panel on the arm of her chair first, then the wheels, then the large base containing a motor. She is confined to a wheelchair, and as much as she would like to accommodate us in our pleas, her running out of here is just as likely as my flying out of here.

"Ma'am, this building is on fire and we all have to get out of here." I step toward the wheelchair and see how hard it will be to maneuver down the stairs. I get on the side of it and attempt a slight lift.

"Holy shit, this thing is heavy!" It doesn't even budge. I try again. No dice.

I step around and kneel down to face her, "Darlin' I would love to take your chair with us, but I don't see how even 4 of us are going to get it down all of these stairs. Now if you don't mind," I put my hand on her leg, "I'm going to lift you out of this chair." She nods her head but doesn't say a word. "Now, is there anything I should know about your condition that would make this hurt at all?"

What do I know? I'm not a doctor. She shakes her head 'no' while I lift her out of the wheelchair and head for the door.

Mike appears after I've lost sight of him again. He has what looks like a large beach folding chair in his hand. He unfolds it creating an emergency wheelchair, with sled blades, rather than wheels, that can slide down stairs. Evidently it had been placed here after the bombing in 1993. I place the woman in the new wheelchair and Mike and I lift her out like a football player coming off the field from an injury.

We head through the hall and back to the stairwell. It seems that the majority of the people above us and below the impact had also heard that this was the way out because the stairwell is now packed with two single file lines, moving, slowly down the stairs. We move so slowly that for the rest of out trip down, we move one flight of stairs at a time and then wait for a minute or so at the next landing until the line shifts again.

For the next 20 floors, my thoughts are consumed with trying to guess where the fire is now. Is it 40 floors above us? 10? Is it even moving? Is it out yet? How the hell does a plane accidentally fly into a building that you notice from miles out? How the hell do you put out a fire in a 110 story building?

I get the answer almost immediately. It's as elementary as it is unbelievable. How do you fight a fire in a 110 story building? Well, it appears the only way is to send firefighters one after another, up the stairs, the many, many stairs, until they find the fire. I can't believe my eyes as, one after another, fully geared firefighters continue to climb the stairs after meeting us on what is now about the 60th floor. At first I'm so glad to see them. Surely they know how to fix this mess. They'll put the fire out in no time. Hell, we'll be at work by next week, if not sooner. My excitement fades as I take note of each one of the firefighter's faces. These aren't the faces of the cocky Irish and Italian guys from the block in Queens that you see catcalling girls from the firehouses in the city. Instead it's a group of somber, exhausted, faces. Their fearful eyes masked by a frozen faced macho façade. Is this what they look like at other fires? Is this worse? Are they just tired from all the stairs? How much further do they have? Do they know? What do they know that we don't?

Life Without Me

I get back to my apartment around 7:00. I'm drunk, tired, my throat and eyes are burning. I am finally all alone. It's so quiet, so thankfully quiet. No sirens, no reporters, no fear of another attack, way uptown away from any notable and potentially targeted landmarks. I appreciate the silence. It's finally the end of the journey from my 100+ block odyssey filled with stops and refreshments along the way.

I'm not sure how long I've been staring at the wall when I get up to take a shower. I'm meeting Mike and his fiancée Joy at a bar to watch the president's address. I wobble to the shower, the long walk and the alcohol making my legs a little weak, I take the most refreshing shower that I've ever had the pleasure to experience.

I can feel the water dissolving the dust in my hair that has made it thicker and so coarse that I can't even run my fingers through it. The water flows from the top of my head, into my eyes, into my mouth, down my throat, cleansing all it can. Cleansing the physical evidence my body has to show for the day. I wait for the water to run across and sting some small wound. Maybe a scrape on my knee, elbow, shoulder, anywhere. Nothing. I've just survived the most devastating terrorist attack with only minutes to spare. . . not one scratch.

The time at the bar is a blur. As soon as I get there, I just want to be alone. No one knows what to say. The three of us sit and mostly just stare at our beer and then the television.

I have to get out, move around. I walk up Second Avenue just past 89th, two blocks away from my place. The image of my dark, small, lonely apartment jolts to my mind. I stop. I don't want to go home. I don't want to be alone right now. As much as I thought I wanted silence, I really just want quiet, but also comfort. I head back down second Avenue and hang a left on 80th. This is my friend Cindy's block. I've not talked to her since my cell phone was left in my office in all this morning's commotion. I ring the buzzer.

"Hello?"

"Hey kid, it's me."

"Who is... John? Oh my God, John!" I can now hear her voice not from the intercom but look up and she's out on her fire escape. "Oh my God, hold on!"

15 seconds later she comes running down the stairs. She opens the door and all but tackles me on the sidewalk. She is bawling.

"John!! I'm so glad to see you!! I heard you were OK from people at home, but I couldn't get in touch with you! I tried to

call! I tried to call you when I saw the planes hit! I saw it John! I
saw the whole thing! "

I try to calm her down. "I know darlin' I know. I
appreciate you trying to call. How many times did you try?"

"I don't know, but finally your voicemail was full so I
couldn't even leave a message."

Oh right. Voicemail. Full?

"Hey, do you mind if I check my messages upstairs?"

"Of course please come up." She looks at me, examining
me to see if and where I was hurt.

"Not a scratch. Not one scratch."

She smiles.

The computerized voice on the end of the cell phone, "You
have 25 messages." I hit "1" to play

8:49 am

"Hey John, it's Dad. Look I just heard something on the radio
about a commuter plane colliding near the World Trade center.
Give me a call when you get a chance."

8:53 am

"Hey man, it's Ben. Dude, I'm looking on the internet and it looks
like you're building's on fire. You do work in tower 1 somewhere
around the 80th floor, right? Hey, give me a call."

8:59 am

124

"John, its Jules, hey, give me a call and let me know you're alright. I'm sure you're not even at work yet, but just give me a ring."

9:00 am

"Hey buddy. Todd here, give me the scoop on what's going on up there. Talk to you soon!"

The messages continue. At 9:05 tower two is hit and the world realizes the devastating fact that we are being attacked.

9:05 am

"Johnny! It's Mom! Baby, please call me as soon as possible. If you're still in your building, please get out!!

9.16 am

"John, hey it's Derek. Man, get the fuck out of there if you've not already, we're being fucking attacked. Please hurry."

9:21 am

"Johnny it's Erica", my sister, "I just hope you're okay. I love you. Call soon!"

9:23 am

"John, it's Jules again, please get out of there. I am freaking out! Please come back. Oh God, please. We love you! Please call soon!"

9:27 am

"Johnny it's Noelle," my other sister, "hey Erica just told me that something's going on in New York. Please get to somewhere safe! I love you!"

9:30 am

"Johnny, it's Dad again. Your mother and I are worried. I'm leaving the office. Get out NOW! Call us at home. Be careful. I love you."

9:38 am

"Dude, it's Todd. I hope you're ok. I really hope you're out of there. This shit is crazy! Call me at the office when you get a chance! Be safe buddy."

9:48 (tower 2 collapses)

"John!," it's Todd again. "Dude, one of the buildings just fell. Pretty sure it's not yours but they are saying that yours might fall too. Dude, get the hell out of there!"

"It's Jules." She's crying, "John, please hurry, please be OK, Oh God please."

"Johnny, it's Michael." My dad's best friend, "Hey brother, we're really worried about you. Hurry up and give your parents a call bud. We miss you."

"John! It's Cindy. I'm watching everything from Times Square! Get out of there and up here as soon as you can!"

"Damnit Johnny." it's Dad, "pick up your Goddamned phone! Just hurry; John! Hurry up!"

The messages continue and increase in urgency, then everyone's tones change.

10:15 (Tower 1 collapses?)

"Uh, John, it's Ben again." He's uneasy, there's no urgency in his voice, more resignation and sadness. "Hey man, I, uh, they said that you're building just collapsed. Hey, I'm sure you're out of there. So, uh, just give us a call when you can. Man. Hope you're ok."

10:16 am
"John, it's Jules." Still crying but she sounds confused, "John, I love you." It's almost like she's talking to herself to make herself feel better. "Please be out of there. Oh God, just please have gotten out of there in time. I miss you. Please be OK, Oh God, please just be OK. I just want to talk."

10:18
"Buddy? It's uh, it's Todd again. Look, if I don't get to...I mean, when you get a chance. I'd just really like to hear from you...again...I mean...just, uh, I'll talk to you soon...I hope."

As the time stamps on the voicemails indicate the later messages, the less hopeful the voices sound. They all think I am dead. I'm one of the few people in the world that ever gets to hear a compilation of eulogies, courtesy of AT&T voicemail.

At no point after 10:15 does either of my parents leave a message. Dad was too busy consoling his wife and himself over what they thought was the loss of their only son.

It finally dawns on me that for a time, almost an hour of my life, the people that mean the most to me thought that I had died. What must they have felt? What must they have thought? What would life be like, without me? Not in a spoiled "I'm the center of the universe" kind of way, but in an existential, "It's a Wonderful Life", alternate reality kind of way. For one hour, in the mind of my loved ones, the world existed without me, leaving nothing but memories, making this day, the period, the "END" of the story that was my life.

What if those last messages on my voicemail really were left in vain? What would my life have amounted to? What memories would people have of me?

"...and we shall remember John for all he meant to us. His smile, his laugh, his sense of humor. The way he could light up a room just with his presence. He was a loving son, brother, a friend. In the name of the Father, the Son, and the Holy Spirit...Amen."

In the pew of St. Michaels, my mother looks ahead to something that's not there. My father is next to her with bloodshot eyes. My sisters are sitting with Julie, all three with their heads down while they cry as if the less they see, the less real this scene will be.

Behind them is my extended family, every neighbor I've even lived near, and over one hundred of my fraternity brothers, friends from high school, and college.

My cousins Anthony and Paul walk up the isle. My buddies Bill, Nick, Todd, Derek, Mike, and Ben follow. They stop at the end of the isle, turn towards the congregation, lift my casket in unison, and walk slowly, silently towards the door in the back of the sanctuary.

Three months later, my mother stares out of the window of a dark house. The only light in the room sneaks through the window from the neighbors' Christmas lights. Neither she nor my father have worked in months. She lifts a glass to her mouth without looking at it and takes a long sip. She can't even smell the alcohol anymore. She can't taste *antything*, can't *feel* anything.

The phone rings. My Dad moves slowly to answer, "John, it's Michael."

"Yeah."

"Buddy, the guys and I are going to grab some oysters and beer down at Tony's."

"Sorry Mike, I can't make it."

"C'mon buddy, I know it's hard, but you have to get out at some point. Especially on the holid…"

"With all do respect Michael," he sounds calm, that changes, "WHAT THE HELL DO YOU KNOW ABOUT WHAT I NEED?!"

"I'm sorry buddy, I didn't mean…"

"No, you didn't. Goodbye."

"Hey guys this is Charles." Derek walks into the house he shares with Mike, Matt, and Cameron near campus. "This is my buddy from Jackson Hole who was gonna come to the Widespread Panic show with us in August but couldn't make it."

Charles walks over to the fridge and leans in to look at some of the pictures.

"Oh wow, that looks like a blast! Man, I would have known most of the people there. I should have come down." He looks closer at the picture, then points. "Yeah, looks like I know most of those guys, except for this one."

"Which one is that?" Derek comes closer.

"This one," he points, "the guy with the big smile. He looks kind of familiar. Does he live around…"

Derek's puts his chin into his chest. Cameron overhears the conversation, gets up and leaves the room. Mike and Matt just look down at the table.

"What?" Charles looks around, confused, and a little nervous, "What'd I say?"

"…we'll pick this up next time. Remember chapters 6, problems 11 through 15. Solutions will be on the class website next week." Accounting 210 class at NC State is dismissed. The class funnels through the door.

"Oh my God, did you hear about that guy?" One blonde co-ed says to her friend.

"No. Which one?"

"The guy from the Towers?"

"Oh yeah," the friend puts her scarf on before going outside, "I heard he's like, still stuck in the debris, or like they figure they might just find his DNA or something."

My sister Erica is behind them. She walks down the hall alone. Looking ahead straight faced with tear filled eyes. No one notices she's even crying.

What if it had really turned out like this? What if I never got to hear those last messages on my voicemail? What would my life have amounted to? What memories would people have of me?

But I *am* still here. I have the power to make new memories, the story continues in spite of the probability.

It's just that I have no idea how to figure out what I want this story to be.

Northbound Decisions

Tom and I drive through Westchester on our way to Newark from Norwalk, CT, to catch our flight back to Atlanta. This isn't exactly the most convenient place to fly out of, but we took what we could get on such short notice. The day before, a client that I had been working on getting a meeting with called to see if we could meet the next day in Connecticut. Tom and I were waiting for our flight in Buffalo back to Atlanta when I got the call. This company in Connecticut had potential to be a big deal and Tom was so excited he told me to call up my contact and tell them that we'd be there. We rented a car and drove the 6 hours starting at 6 that night, to get down to Connecticut. We had to stop half way at a mall to buy clothes for the morning since our luggage was already on the Atlanta bound flight.

"Hey," Tom said, "Don't worry about the money. It's just money. Time... *Time* is our most precious currency."

I agree with him, especially since I'm not the one shelling out for the new duds.

"Time is our most precious currency." Tom repeats this credo the next day in the conference room of our potential Norwalk based client. We are presenting our sales consulting program and he is describing the theory behind spending your time on qualified customers, the theory being that 'the customer's always right, until it's not cost effective to make him right anymore.'

"If a salesperson is spending time trying to force a customer to buy a product that isn't appropriate for their needs, this salesperson is wasting his most precious commodity…Time."

The seven heads around the conference table nod in agreement.

"We teach that time," Tom continues after reading the crowd, "is our most precious currency not only in business, but in life." The nodding heads are now smiling

An hour later Tom and I are sitting in traffic on the Hudson parkway. "Buddy! That, was a great meeting. I have got to tell you, we are going to make you some nice coin off of this one."

"Yeah, I hope so," I say less than enthused.

Tom told me when I was hired that if I was able to find a company with certain characteristics and we got them to agree to a meeting that he would close them and I could count the money as made. Well this is the fourth time having arranged such meetings and so far I've not seen one consulting contract come from my efforts. In Tom's defense, Aslan did win these contracts eventually, I'm just too impatient to wait it out, not being prepared for the time it takes a company to free up consulting dollars.

"What's wrong buddy?" Tom is truly concerned at my tone. He's told me that he's very impressed with how I'm able to engage high level customers and loves my work ethic. He does his best to keep me motivated even in the face of delayed contracts and working in a small room with little more than a phone and computer in Marietta, GA. I've told him before that I miss New York and eventually want to go back and he's made it very clear that he will do what it takes to keep me.

"It's the New York thing again." His face looks like the face of a dad whose kid tells him he wants to go to a college half way across the country. Faking encouragement to do what makes you happy, while deep down being so opposed to that choice that it's hard to hide that feeling behind any words to the contrary.

"You really miss it huh?"

We approach a sign announcing the exit to the city.

"I do. I really do. Before...you know...before I left New York I had the best time. I loved the energy, the history, knowing that everyday had brought the possibility of a little adventure. It's just the best place I've ever lived. And I kind of left before I was really ready to."

"And Atlanta's not doing it for you?" He almost looks like his feelings are hurt. Tom was born, raised, went to college, and now lives with his family in Atlanta.

"It's not that it's a bad place. It's just... well it's just not New York." I say this as we pass over the George Washington Bridge and I see the skyline to my left. Tom sees me looking longingly out the window to the city.

"Johnny boy!" Tom says like an old high school football coach, "We love you kid, we really do. And the guys and I would hate to lose you. Now I've told you before that after we get a few contracts under our belts, you could do this job anywhere, New York, Alaska, hell Nova Scotia for all we care. It's just going to take some time."

But I want to go now! Tom can tell and continues…

"But buddy, we teach in our program that time is your most precious currency. Not just in business but in life." He almost hesitates, fighting with whether to send his son to the opposite coast college or to discourage the idea for his own selfish reasons. "Buddy, if getting back to New York is going to make you that much happier than being in Atlanta, with us," nice attempt at guilt there pal, you sure you're not Italian? "then you might want to consider not wasting any more of *your* precious time wishing you were somewhere else."

"Really Tom… you wouldn't be mad at me if I left?"

"Disappointed? Yes. Would I miss you being around? Absolutely. Mad? Not a bit."

Moving Back to NYC

After a lackluster year in Atlanta, my second stint in New York is everything I want it to be. Having lived here briefly I already know that lay of the land so I'm better prepared to find an apartment. I move back to the city with three suitcases, ready to start over.

I crash with a buddy of mine for a couple of weeks while I search for and find an apartment share on Craigslist, the single greatest open market website in the world if you live in any major city for the fact that it is easy, there is a wealth of apartments and used products, and most importantly, it's free.

I find a temporary place to stay in Hells Kitchen but the first week I'm there I pop into a bar in the neighborhood and run into my buddy Drew from college. He's in the city acting which means he's a full time bar tender. I pull up a seat and have a drink. We get to talking and he tells me that he shares a six bedroom, three bathroom place down in the East Village, which is in my opinion, a way cooler place to party than a few blocks from tourist central Time's Square where we are now. Drew says that one of the roommates is moving back to Ireland so he's actually looking to fill two spots and if I want one it's mine.

This is exactly what I'm looking for, a place further downtown, with roommates. I didn't have any roommates in Atlanta and it got pretty boring. This way there would always be something going on, somebody doing something, anything.

I move in a week later. The place is exactly what I want. Large living room, kitchen, and a large back deck complete with cartoonish mural, grill, Christmas lights, and even a hammock. Who the hell has a hammock in NYC? I do.

The neighborhood is filled with mostly young people who tend to be musicians, actors, writers, painters, dancers and everyone seems pretty interesting. I love it. My roommates are pretty cool, too. Like I said, Drew is an actor from North Carolina, Steve is a model from Washington Heights, Andrew is an investment banker from Dublin, Ireland, Andrea is a hippie writer from Gainesville, Florida, and Kristy is a nurse from Indiana. Later the hippie writer is replaced by TJ, the chef and restaurateur from Baltimore. I don't think you could find a more diverse group of people without a formal casting call.

I'm getting closer to finding what makes me happy. Great culture, great nightlife, and interesting people. Unfortunately I'm losing touch with one of the things that already makes me happy... Jules. She's adjusting well to law school, finding her friends, including the drunk-ass, Jason is his name, who I guess didn't seem

137

that bad. I met all of her friends including Jason who, just as I figured, was in the corner of the bar, close to passing out. Your typical trust fund, private school, preppy douche bag. The kind of kid that makes up for his lack of good looks with fostering everybody's perception that he has money, not to mention debilitating alcoholism.

Hey, what's not to love? But what right do I have to question her friends? I'm 500 miles away, having the time of my life. My job, my apartment, my friends, my life. I love it all. I'm just glad she has some people to hang out with. While I'm off finding myself.

I make the neighborhood my home. My coffee shop, my deli, my gym, my bars. I make friends mostly with people in the neighborhood. It's refreshing and inspiring to meet so many people that are doing exactly what they want in life, chasing their dreams, to become a film star, an author, a stand up comedian, or whatever the hell it is they want to be. What I like the best is that most of these people aren't doing if for the fame, but for the lifestyle of doing what makes you happy even if they don't make it big. It is the happiest and most comfortable I've felt in a long time. We always hear about people not being happy where they are, professionally, emotionally, physically. America and maybe the entire world is a place, like Train says "where what we want is what we want until it's ours," and then we find something else to want. But for me this is different, for now at least. I couldn't imagine myself being happier at this point in my life than right here. Will I stay here forever? No. But there is a certain satisfaction that comes with knowing that you are living the exact right *way* for you at the exact right *time*.

My buddy's father put it into perspective for me once He said, "While you might party a little more at some point, be able to afford more things, or get laid a little more, if you spend your whole life trying to time when you're going to be the happiest, you'll just be chasing your tails. Don't wait for the time when you think you're going to be the happiest, and don't look back longingly for the last time you think you were. Just do your best to make *every* time in your life the happiest."

I get off the N/R train from the theatre district where I joined a friend of mine for a showing of *Wicked*. I head east then walk down avenue B through the falling snow. It's the beginning of the first big snow of the season. Drew is outside a bar across the street smoking a cigarette. He sees me.

"Johnny," He waves with the hand holding the cigarette then flicks the butt in the street. "Come on in, we're all meeting for a little nightcap."

I walk inside and take off my scarf, gloves, and jacket before I pull a stool up to the bar. All six of us roommates are here. Steve is the bartender and we are the only people in the bar. We sit, talk, tell jokes, laugh. For a couple of hours, six of some of the least likely friends in the world, own their little space in the Big Apple.

The Blind Leading the Blind

Late December, and Julie has taken the weekend from law school to come spend some time with me in the city. We are heading back downtown from the Upper East side after a Sunday dinner with friends. It's about 11:00 and even though the 6 stop on 77th is in a safe neighborhood, it's always just a little too quiet for me at night and kind of gives me the creeps. I can tell Julie feels the same as she grips my arm when we pass a homeless guy on the steps of the library heading up Lexington.

"I just couldn't imagine walking around all by myself at night up here."

"Aww, it's not bad, it's just a little quiet since this is a safe neighborhood where families actually live and go to sleep earlier that the crazy asses down by me."

"Well at least you feel a little safer in Alphabet city with people always walking around, even if they are blue haired transvestites and strung out hipsters."

I turn to her with a scolding look. I would love to stay in New York for a long time, but she wants to practice law in North Carolina. Even though the decision is at least 2 years away, there is tension when she lists the reasons she doesn't like the city and when I list the reasons why North Carolina is boring.

"Here we go." I point to the subway entrance and lead us down.

After 10 minutes of waiting for the 6 train on its Sunday night schedule, one comes and we get on. There's no one else in the car but us and a late 20 something blind man.

Julie looks at me to acknowledge her concern for him. Knowing how she feels after her comment about how uncomfortable she would be navigating Manhattan by herself I can tell she is worried about this guy doing so alone too. I, for the time being, just assume keep with New Yorker fashion and mind my own business. Until...

"Excuse me sir?"

Is he talking to me? I guess so.

"Yeah brother, what can I do for you?"

"Which side does the train open?"

Julie looks at me with the most sad puppy dog eyes.

"Well that depends. Where're you getting off?"

"Grand Central to Metro North back to Westchester."

Westchester! How the hell does a blind guy who doesn't know the trains like the back of his hand come all the way to the city on his own from Westchester! What if he was the only one on the train? What if he was mugged? He was coming from further uptown than us since we got on the train after him, but how far uptown? Too much further and you get into some pretty rough areas…particularly if you can't see danger coming at you. Julie looks at me hoping that I have the answer.

"I'm pretty sure it opens on the right at Grand Central, but honestly man, I'm not sure."

Man, if he's not sure what side the door opens how is he going to get to his connection? I've never even taken Metro North since I never go to the northern suburbs so I'm not really sure how to get there. I usually take Penn Station New Jersey Transit lines over to Jersey. Now *that* I could give him directions for.

I can't just leave this guy wandering Grand Central in the middle of the night. I want to offer help but the last thing I want to do is insult the guy. Maybe he doesn't need my help at all. But the door? Why doesn't he know where the door is? 'Okay,' I think, 'would I rather risk insulting this guy, or spend the rest of the night, week, month, or however long wondering if he got home alright?'

"Hey," I say "can I give you a hand to your connection?" I wish that I could take back the words as soon as they're out of my mouth. There is silence and I can't tell if he's insulted, hurt, or…

"Actually," he says sheepishly "if you're getting off here would you mind?"

142

Thank God. Thank God that I'm not getting yelled at on the train by some random blind guy about how I'm insulting him for underestimating his ability. And thank God that I asked since he really could use the help.

"Oh yeah, man no problem, this is my stop anyway." I assume that white lies under these circumstances are fine.

"Thanks." He smiles. "Is this her stop, too? She sounds pretty."

"Yeah, she's coming. And she's alright I guess. " Julie elbows me in the side and I turn and smile.

The train stops and we get off.

"Hey sir."

"It's John."

"Okay John, I'm Robert...would you mind if...if I grab your arm to lead me upstairs."

"Yeah, man. Not a problem."

Julie and I walk him up to Metro North. Through conversation we find out that he's a disk jockey for some college radio show. He gets along well, he says, just doesn't come to the east side much so he's not very familiar with the 6.

After a moment, Robert seems to get his bearings and knows where he is just as soon as we get to the ticketing area.

"Okay, John, I'm good from here."

"You sure?" I ask concerned trying so hard not to seem condescending.

"I could do it with my eyes closed."

A sense of humor, huh? I guess it helps to be a little funny as a DJ.

"Alright man, well you have a good evening, see you around."

"Not if I see you first." He smiles and walks away.

Jules and I wait a little while. I just want to make sure that he's really alright.

All of a sudden I get a weird feeling, kind of emotional. How do you like that? I guess people don't mind help, as long as you don't make them feel helpless. I'm touched by the thought, touched by the pride I feel for him to overcome what I would consider to be a huge challenge.

And then it hits me. I actually care about this stranger, this person that I'll probably never see again. After all of this survivor's guilt mixed with the guilt of being undeservingly labeled a hero, despite some of the stupid shit I've done and sometimes continue to do, I actually might really be a good person. Not just someone that people think is a good person, but a truly caring, compassionate human being. Not just for television appearances or magazine interviews, but when nobody is watching, no Oprah, no People magazine, just me in my truest self.

Okay, so my girl was watching, but still. . .

Up until now I didn't really know what an epiphany was. But now it's as clear as it can be. That was the piece I was missing in my post 9/11 new life goals. I had become so focused on living life to the fullest and put so much emphasis on everything I wanted to do, and things that suited me, but now I realize that it is really true that helping people really feels good and that I can get used to doing more of this. Not just through charity work but by seeing life through different eyes. Not just what's in it for me but really thinking about how I might help others.

This is what life is about. This is self actualization in its purest form. I heard a quote once that says something to the effect that "People don't remember who you are half as much as they remember how you make them feel." This is the key to immortality. This is the key to a full life, leaving people you encounter with a great impression of someone they can count on to be there for them. Not just because it helps them at the moment, but because it is evidence that in the midst of crime, cancer, poverty, and even terrorist attacks, this world isn't such a bad place after all.

Can somebody help me off of this soap box? It's scary up here.

No Easy Way Out

"Hey man." I grab one of the firefighters who turns a seems to look right through me. "Look, I know the elevator is out from above, but do any of the express elevators from the 44th floor work?"

He doesn't even look me in the eye as he silently shakes his head. Shit! I though maybe we could grab an elevator further down to take us the rest of the way. Well we at least have to stop to make a phone call and let someone outside know that we're alright. Mike and I reach the 55th floor, step out of the stairwell with our traveling companion and try to find an office with a working phone. Despite the appearance of the office and the power being out, the phones do work. I finally reach my father.

"Dad! It's me!"

"Are you alright?" He's calm. He's always calm in an emergency. The only difference is that everything he says sounds is like he's reprimanding me.

"Yeah, I'm fine. We're coming down the stairs right now." I'm trying not to sound scared.

"Fine. Just move quickly. Do you understand me? Quickly." Again he sounds like he's rushing me, like he's trying to get me ready for church as a kid. He's not yelling, just very matter of fact. He's very calm, but abbreviates the conversation.

"I will Dad."

"Go. I love you." He hangs up.

It was probably a good idea he didn't tell me everything he's seen on the news. That this isn't the work of an errant prop plane. That my building and the country is being attacked by planes hijacked by terrorists as is our next door twin, World Trade Center 2.

Mike and I hang up the phones and head back toward the stairwell with the woman and the chair. We head down several more flights and stop as we've done over almost the last half hour or so. I'm now getting more worried. I just wish we were out of here. I begin to notice how confined we are, how crowded it is, and the fact that we are standing absolutely still. My mind moves back to wondering what's going on upstairs. Is the fire gaining on us? I hate not knowing.

I begin to pJay, something I'd not done in quite sometime. 'God, please, You have to stay with me. This isn't a pJayer request like hoping to pass a test or getting a job, I need You to answer this right now. God, please keep me calm, please don't let me lose it in here. There's no way I'm going to make it if I don't keep cool. I need You. I need You now.'

I'm immediately calm. I feel safe. I focus on the task at hand. One step at a time, I look down at my foot, just one step at a... I begin to feel my foot vibrating. I feel, then hear a rumbling.

It's getting louder. What the hell is that? Is a floor above us collapsing? Where is that sound coming from?

The heavy steel door leading to the hallway bursts open propelled by a strong current of air bringing with it dust and debris. The force is so strong that it makes the door look like a flimsy piece of cardboard. The small stairwell is being flooded with dust making it hard to see anything. It's loud. Like being in the middle of a tornado. Mike and I, along with several other men force the door shut and the commotion in the stairwell stops. Everyone is silent, their wide, dazed eyes serving as the only hint of their thoughts. Without a word we all head down the stairs.

After a long while of constant movement we are stopped again. Firefighters have set up a sort of triage area. No one is really injured but some older people are there resting and getting water. One of the firefighters sees Mike and I with our passenger.

"Hey ma'am, we have a little area set up to take a rest. You can hang out here with me or one of the other guys can take you the rest of the way." He looks up to Mike and I, "and it'll give these guys a bit of a rest too."

She looks at the firefighter and seems deep in thought. She's not said two words to Mike or me this whole time. But I feel like she wants to say something. She and I lock eyes and I can feel her asking me something.

"Look sweetheart, you're more than welcome to break up with us now." I smile to her and then to Mike to see if what I'm going to say is okay with him, too. He smiles indicating that it is.

"But Mike and I are going down these stairs and getting out of this building ASAP. Now this guy does have his fancy hat," I smile to the firefighter so he knows I'm just kidding, "but if you'll let us, I'm sure we can get you out of here just as well."

She smiles, almost embarrassed to answer. "Yes please." She says so quietly that I'm not sure if I hear it or just read her lips.

"Well what are we waiting for? Mikey you ready to go?"

"You lead the way kid."

As we head further down the stairs they become wet and the lights go dim. We are getting lower in the building and it looks like the power's going in and out. We go lower still and before we enter through a doorway to an even darker hallway I notice that my feet are wet, then my ankles, then just above my ankles. The door slams shut behind me. We're almost out, we're almost down.

The only light I see is from one single flashlight in a long dark corridor moving sporadically back and forth...

Southbound Again. . .

Even though I loved living in Manhattan, I knew it wasn't forever. Since the time I had moved away, Raleigh, specifically its downtown, had grown considerably and I began to realize that Raleigh really is a great place to live. I knew that eventually I would end up in North Carolina, be closer to my family, go to business school, build a good life in Raleigh, but I felt a pressure, real or otherwise, that shortly after I would be engaged and then married to Julie and I wasn't sure I was ready for that just yet. I mean, I've moved to a different city every year for that last 3 years. I'm not sure that I can commit to being in any one place for any length of time.

Despite my concern, I put the plan to get back to Raleigh in place. I get a job as a loan officer and financial advisor with a bank, find a temporary place to live with my old fraternity brothers. As my move inches closer those old reservations begin to surface.

"John, something's not right, I can tell."

She is right. "Baby, I don't know what it is."

"I don't believe you! You do know what it is. You just don't want to tell me." Her voice is quivering, she starts to cry.

"Baby, don't cry. Please."

"Why John? I can tell something's wrong, and has been for a while now. What is it? Just say it!"

I don't want to say it, I can't say it, I have to say it, how do I say it? "Jules, I just don't know…I just don't know if…if I'm…if I'm in love with you anymore."

I want to take it back so badly. That's not what I mean! I just need some time! I'm going back home and I'm scared, scared of feeling defeated again, scared of feeling like a failure, I have to make home *my* home, on *my* terms. But I can't tell her that. She'll say that I can do this with her, even though both of us know I can't.

"Just give me some time."

"How…*sob*…much…*sob*…time do you think it will take?" God this is killing me! I love her so much, she's my best friend. I hate making her feel this way.

"I don't know…don't wait for me…I don't know. I mean…don't worry…. everything will be OK."

Breaking Up, Breaking Down

Two months later I move back to Raleigh. I drive in at midnight, drop my bags, and it's like nothing's changed. Except for Raleigh is considerably cooler than when I left. More bars, condos, a more vibrant downtown, not to mention all of my idiot friends are now idiot friends with jobs, money, and the means for us all to have a great time. And a great time we have. Jules and I keep in touch, but don't see each other for a while. It's been a month since I've moved back and her birthday is coming up. I'm beginning to feel comfortable in Raleigh, comfortable with me being in Raleigh. I think more and more about how I miss seeing Julie and feel like this is a great time to pick up where we left off. I decide to give her a call.

"John. Oh, hey!" She sounds strange, like she's not exactly happy to hear from me.

"Hey, is this a good time?"

"Of course."

"Well I just wanted to call you and say happy early birthday."

"Thank you." She seems genuinely appreciative for the call.

"Well, hey, I was wondering if you'd let me come to Winston to take the birthday girl out for a fun birthday weekend."

"Oh, that's very sweet of you." Very sweet of me? She sounds like I've offered to watch her dog. I hate talking like we're acquaintances.

"Well great, when would you like to do it? Since your birthday is in the middle of the week I was thinking either this weekend or next?"

She is silent

"Jules? You there?"

She sighs, "John, I...I have something to tell you." I've never heard this tone before. It's formal, business like, not familiar. This is not good.

"John, I'm seeing someone."

The words hit me like buckshot to the chest. I can actually feel a tightening in the upper area of my abdomen.

"What? Who? How? Since when?"

"It doesn't matter who."

Doesn't matter who? We've been best friends for 7 years.

"Bullshit! I think I have a right to know who you've been seeing behind my back!"

"Behind your back?! You broke up with me! And from what I hear you've not been necessarily celibate since you moved back home!"

"That's beside the Goddamned point." Of course because I don't want to talk about it. "Do I know this asshole? Who the hell is it!?"

She pauses and the yelling stops, she knows this is the big blow…"It's Jason."

It is the big blow, I can barely speak. This 'friend' of hers that has been there all along.

"No. No, you're kidding me. This whole time probably… before we even…I can't believe…Jules, no, please, you…you can't do this."

"I'm sorry John. He's been there for me. I know you had to 'find yourself' but I've been so lonely. I needed you, and you just weren't there."

"Baby, I know," I'm getting desperate, "I know, but I'm here now. I'm back and I'm doing what you've wanted me to do. I'm happy here now, I'm not going to leave again, I promise." I'm like a child trying to argue away the divorce of his parents. "I'll be better, I won't go nuts anymore. I won't pick up and leave again. Please! We can fix this. It's not too late."

Julie starts to cry.

"John, you told me not to wait for you! You said you had to get things straight! What was I supposed to do?"

"We've been broken up for TWO MONTHS! A lot I fucking mean to you if after two months you can be over me so quickly."

"John, we both know that this has been coming for more than two months! I just can't be second choice to you anymore. I understand that you have to find what you want, but I wanted to be

WHAT YOU WANT!" She stops yelling again, now to almost a sniffling whisper. "I've not been what you wanted in a long time, you know that as well as I do, and my heart just can't take it anymore."

She's right. I've ignored her, been so selfish in my quest for my own happiness. I have no answer to this.

"Jules?"
"I can't."
"Jules please."
"I'm sorry John."
"Don't do this. Please."
"I have to go."

Silence

And I thought I couldn't feel worse than I did on that clear Tuesday morning just over 4 years ago.

The emotional parallels after 9/11 and for the next few months are remarkably close. It's the same feeling of depression except at least after 9/11 I had support. Not only had I been an innocent victim, but I came out regarded as a hero. But now, this situation is all my fault. I did this. There are no candlelight vigils, no inspirational stories, nothing. Just me and the knowledge that I'd made what I considered the biggest mistake of my life.

I try to occupy my time, which I now have much more of since I can't seem to sleep anymore, working out and doing charity work which I figure could be a good side effect of the emotional hell I'm dealing with. If there is one thing 9/11 taught me it's that you can either have your pain slowly beat you, or you can attack it hard, and beat your pain. However, in this yin and yang world, with the good, comes the bad and the time not spent doing anything productive is spent drinking. I spend every day feeling like I can't breathe and it's the only other thing I can think of that I can use to keep me from suffocating.

In the Rubble. . .

Shit, I still can't breathe, it hurts to try. 'Okay God, I'm yours, let's do it.' What will my funeral be like? Will I go to heaven? OK, try to breath one more time...no dice. I miss you Mom, I miss you Dad, I love you both...Alright God, do your thing.

"Oh my God! We're going to die!" I hear a man's voice say. It's the guy next to me behind the van. For the last few seconds I've resigned myself to the fact that I'm dying, but now that someone else is now telling me when I'm going to die, I become defiant. My defiance gives me strength, and some hope. If this guy can talk, he can obviously breathe. I must have just inhaled at the wrong time. There has to be clean air somewhere. I begin to crush the debris in my mouth with my teeth as it dissolves in my saliva. I spit most of it out but swallow a little until I can move my mouth freely. I still can't see but I get up from the ground and walk in a direction that I believe to be uptown. Maybe I can walk far enough away that this cloud, the size of which I have no idea, will end. It doesn't take long to see that this idea might have some kinks in it as

I run into a series of sidewalk planted trees, street signs, and then trip over something and fall back to the ground. I realize that the "something" that I tripped on feels unusual. It's like a garbage bag, maybe a piece of furniture, or. . . I reach down to touch it. It's the familiar touch of a leg. Holy shit! Oh God it is a person. Which way did I walk? Is this person dead? What the hell is going on?

I grab the leg and begin to shake it. "Hey! Hey, can you hear me? Are you okay?" There's no answer. They must be...Oh God please don't be...

"Shut the fuck up and sit the fuck down!" says a voice with a thick accent unmistakably from Queens as the leg shakes violently from my grip. I feel a hand grab my face. I resist and then feel what seems like a plastic bubble over my mouth and nose. "Breathe in." says the voice. He takes the gas mask away and I hear him take a deep breath. "I'm an EMT, just sit down and keep your mouth and eyes closed until this passes. The last one cleared up after a few minutes.

The last one?

"The last what?" I say confused

"I said Shut Up!"

He's right. Minutes later the complete darkness under which we exist is pierced by several Jays of light. The number of Jays increase slowly, independently, until they merge to create one source of light illuminating my surroundings just enough to allow me to make out the shapes of objects and people around me.

"Johnny! John! Are you alright!?" I hear Mike from the distance and look to my left. I can make out a figure crawling out from underneath a fire truck and I stumble towards him.

"Mike! Are you okay?"

"Yeah, kid," He pats me on the back as if congratulating me for a good game, "You?"

I look down at what I can see of myself in the thick haze "Good, I think."

I can make out the street and orient myself to which way is uptown and away from the building.

"Let's get moving, huh?" I say.

"Sounds good to me."

Mike and I slowly walk uptown. I'm in my tee shirt after having taken off my button up to tie around my face in the building. Mike still has on his tie and has his computer bag with him, amazingly enough.

We walk through debris and pass cars and buildings that look like they've been through a nuclear blast. As we move further uptown the haze dissipates but my sight is still blurred from the debris stuck in my eyes. I try to wipe my eyes but there isn't a square inch of my hand, or my body, not covered by a thick coat of dust. I can make out a crowd of people a block or so up from us on the West Side Highway. They are behind police barricades. It seems that the police have designated that area as the closest point to the towers one could go and still be safe. Any further and they would be in the danger zone. Any further and they would be in as much danger as we had been. There is a mass of ambulances, news vans, police vans, and fire trucks. As we approach the barricades the crowd seems to get even more restless, eager to touch us like we're movie stars on a red carpet, except these people don't want autographs, they want to give us the medical attention they think we need and ask us questions we can't possibly answer. As soon as we cross through the barricades we are assaulted by a mass of reporters and paramedics.

"What was it like? What did you see? How do you feel?" The slew of questions come rapid fire. I push away the microphones shoved in my face. I have to get to a phone and call my parents. "Sir! What's your name? What company do you work for? Are you hurt?"

My vision is still blurred from the debris and the noise. The crowd is making it difficult to know where I am. "Leave me alone! I need to get to a phone!"

"Do you know where everyone in your office is? Do you know if you've lost anyone? Where do you think the terrorists will strike next?"

Whoa, terrorists? Can we go back to that? I turn to the reporter.

"What? What do you mean? What terrorists?"

She doesn't answer my question but asks another one. "Do you think they knew how to take down *both* of the buildings?"

Both? What the hell is she talking about? I turn around. The cloud is getting smaller. I can see far enough to see that neither my building, nor tower two are still standing. What the...*BOTH*? I didn't even notice when I came out of my building that Tower two had already collapsed. Having exited on the northwest corner, Tower 1 always obstructed Tower 2 to the southeast. I had no way of knowing that it had already collapsed.

Terrorists? I'm overwhelmed. I feel angry, sad, scared, powerful, and vulnerable all at once. I have to get out of here.

"Sir," a woman in a paramedic uniform rushes up to me with a large bottle of some type of solution. "Sir, you need to flush your eyes out and then drink this." She starts pouring the solution over my head. It's cold and it flows down my face stinging my eyes and loosening the particles under and around my eye lids. I blink repeatedly to help the process. Shit! This stuff stings!

"Now sir you have to drink this." She starts to pour some liquid toward my mouth, but I keep my mouth closed like a baby who doesn't want his vegetables and the liquid runs down my face, neck, and shirt. Some of the liquid makes it's way into my mouth. It's salty and tastes awful. I spit the small amount out.

"Lady, don't you have a Gatorade or something? Hell, even a friggin' Diet Coke?"

"Sir this is a solution to induce vomiting. You've ingested some pretty unhealthy stuff and we have to get it out."
I concede and slug down the nasty salty drink

"Look sweetheart, how much more unhealthy can anything be than a Coney Island hot...BLUUURRRRUUUUAAAAHH"

Pitch black vomit, like tar, spews from my mouth. I don't know if I'm more terrified that this stuff is coming out of me, or that it was in me to begin with.

"Oh my God!", shrieks the young blonde reporter who was hassling me a minute ago.

I let the salty drink's affects run it's course and rest for a second, holding my position bent over and bracing myself with my hands on my knees. I stand up straight and look at the, now speechless, reporter.

"If you want to do something useful," I wipe my mouth with the back of my hand, "find out what happened to the ambulance that was waiting at the west entrance of Tower 1. There's a handicapped women that we brought out of the building in there. We don't know her name, but please try to find her." The reporter nods, almost in a daze brought on by the day's events, the black vomit, or maybe the potential story developing in her head after what I just told her.

I turn to Mike, "We have to find a phone." Mike points to a service station on the east side of the street. We both head towards it. As I walk, the combination of my sweat, the fine dust from the building, and the salty solution turns my shirt into a hardening shell. The attendants let us into the service station.

"Hey, you guys alright?" The attendant says with the wide eyes of a little kid. I pass a mirror and stop. I look like a moving statue. I am coated with dust and my eyes are bright red. My hair is matted down with chunks of what looks like concrete. I see a shower and strip off my shirt to rinse off.

"Hey, do you guys have a working phone in here?" Mike asks.

"Yeah, back in the office. Have at it." Everyone in the station is looking at us like we're a freak show.

We walk back to the office, grab the phone, and dial my Dad's office.

"Hello?" It's not the receptionist, it's Michael, my Dad's best friend, practically my second father, who happens to work with him as well.

"Mike! It's Johnny!"

"Johnny!" he yells away from the phone. "It's Johnny!! Hey, he's okay!" I hear a round of applause from the office in the background. "Hey buddy. We were so worried about you! So glad you're okay. Were you far away from the building when it collapsed?"

I think for a minute. No. No I wasn't far away at all. It hits me that I was about as close as I could have been to that building without losing my life. The thought overwhelms me and I let out a sound that's half sob and half yell.

"No!!! No!!! I was so close Mike! So close you wouldn't believe!"

"Oh buddy!" He's getting choked up, "Buddy, I'm so sorry! I'm so sorry. I'm so glad your okay. I'm going to conference you in with your parents, they're both at home. Hold on a sec."

The phone clicks and doesn't get past half a ring.

"Hello!" it's my Dad

"Dad! Dad, it's me!!"

"Johnny? Johnny!!" He says it like he can't believe it's me. Like he'd never hear from me again. I can hear my mother screaming hysterically in the background.

"Son! Are you OK!" He's not calm anymore. Crisis mode is over now. The emotional walls are collapsing.

"I'm fine Dad! I'm just fine. I miss you guys."

"Johnny!" My mother grabs and screams into the phone. She keeps repeating my name like the more she says it the more true it is that I'm here.

"Baby! Can you hear me! I love you baby!! My sweat boy!! I love you!"

"I love you too Ma!," I choke through tears, "I'm coming home. I'm coming the hell home!!"

After the phone calls, Mike and I head back out to the street and continue uptown. My apartment is about 95 blocks up and east and with the interruption of mass transit, the only option we have is to walk. The street is filled with people in pandemonium and a herd of people is running past us.

"The street is going to blow up!" Screams a voice from the crowd

"A gas line is broken in building 7! Everybody move!" another voice yells.

Yesterday, of course, I couldn't imagine the street actually exploding, but something tells me that I'm going to see a few more things I've not seen before.

164

Naïve in Vegas

The spring before my 26th birthday, my buddies Nick, Bill and I
decided that we needed a weekend in Vegas. With Nick in Dallas
and Bill in Atlanta the three of us don't see each other very often
and try to get together at least every year or so since we graduated
college. With work schedules and the like the only time we can
find that works for our Vegas trip is Easter weekend. I'm certain
that there are more appropriate ways to celebrate the resurrection of
our Lord and Savior than in the home of excessive gambling,
drinking, and legalized prostitution, but hey, schedules are tight.

Friday evening I land in the Las Vegas airport and grab a
cab to meet Nick and Bill at the hotel. Bill was able to score a great
deal on a huge multi room suite in the Bellagio, and I can't wait to
see it. I can see the lights from the highway and minutes later we're
on the strip. It's bright and there are a lot of people, but what hits
me isn't the size, which is dwarfed by Times Square, but the fact
that everyone looks thrilled to be there. It's like *Girls Gone Wild*
except with adults.

"Where ya staying buddy!" The cabby asks.

"The Bellagio"

"Very nice! Ever been to Vegas?"

"Nope"

He turns around with an excited and mischievous grin "Well buckle up brother, you can lose your soul in this town."

"Happy Easter!" I say as I slam the cab door in front of the hotel and light a cigarette. I was a little tired coming off the plane but in front of the famous Bellagio Hotel and Casino, I'm wide awake.

Nick answers the phone. "Hey, what's the room number?"

"Dude this place is fucking sick! You won't believe it! Hurry your ass up, we have a drink waiting for you and we'll get the hell back downstairs."

The first time in Vegas is a lot like the first time you have sex. You're been looking forward to it for a long time, have heard everyone talk about it like it's the greatest thing in the world, and when you finally get there it's as good as you ever thought and better.

From the moment I get there, the first night is a blur of booze, gambling, girls, music, money, more gambling, and more booze. Nick, Bill, and I fared alright on the tables. We lost a little, won a little, but pretty much broke even if you consider all the 'free' booze we had. We went to the club "Light" which I wasn't too impressed with. It was a mass of short little meatheads with tight shirts and glow sticks. The music was that crazy techno/house bullshit that makes me feel like someone's grandpa when it gives me a headache, and the group of assholes that had those annoying whistles that people bring to raves did not help matters any. The three of us decided to head out of there and get to sleep since now it's about 4 in the morning. We get a little sidetracked at a blackjack table and finally get to bed around 6.

The next day, my splitting headache wakes me up at 10:00.

"Dude, I can't feel my heart." I yell to Nick and Bill in the other rooms.

"It's alright buddy, let's go downstairs and get some food." Bill yells back.

We get ready and head downstairs and get off the elevator feeling like the 21st century Rat Pack in jeans. The lobby is bustling with families and proves to be too much for our hung over senses to handle. We can't justify gambling or drinking at 10:30 in the morning so we head out to the pool.

After about an hour at the pool we all start to get the Vegas itch.

"Hey guys." Bill says

I lift my head off the chair. It feels like it weighs a hundred pounds.

"Yeah buddy?"

"You guys, getting bored out here?"

We think for a little bit. Nick shrugs his shoulders.

"Yeah, a little bit."

"What do you wanna do?" I ask.

Bill looks off as he thinks.

"Well we could…if you guys didn't think it was too early…"

"Blackjack?" Nick blurts out.

"Done" I say and turn to Bill.

"Done" the three of us jump up and run inside like the place is closing in 5 minutes.

We gamble and drink from 11:30 in the morning until 7:30 at night, stopping only to get ready to go out and then we resume festivities. This night is a little more our style than the night before. We find a little lounge in the hotel that's more low key and conducive to conversation. This is more our speed than the "oonst oonst" beat of the techno from last night. We find a group of girls from Mississippi on spring break and spend most of the night with them.

Nothing happens with any of us but hey, most of us have girlfriends and most of them have boyfriends. What the hell happened to 'what happens in Vegas stays in Vegas?' Oh well, it's getting to be about 6:00 in the morning anyway. Time to go to bed. Nick heads up early so it's just Bill and me wandering aimlessly through the lobby of the Bellagio. We play a hand here and there, but decide that we're just too tired, hungry, both, or neither. We're just getting close to that Vegas-up-too-long-zombie mode. This state is encouraged, I've heard, by the casino's pumping in oxygen near the tables to keep people up long enough to make some stupid decisions. Luckily it doesn't work every time.

The area with the tables, although open all night, is populated with few other people than me, Bill, the dealers, guys with the vacuums, and one or two cocktail waitresses. After a quick hand of blackjack that we both end up losing, Bill and I find ourselves at the table with two smoking hot blondes, in their early twenties, dressed to the nines in black cocktail dresses, and with the energy of a freshly primped sorority girls right before a big night on the town. We're both actually too zoned out to really notice until I see that the dealer has stopped the game temporarily and is just smiling at Bill and me.

"I said…'How's your luck been tonight gentlemen?' " says the blonde with straight hair as she pulls out a cigarette from her little purse with the silver chain strap.

I snap out of it and look over. She's talking to us. I try to muster a charming smile, but I have a feeling I look more like the apes at the zoo showing their teeth when you piss them off.

"Oh, our luck has been pretty good. Win some, lose some. You know this town." I try to say it like I'm an old pro.

"You can say that again." The blonde with the curly hair now says, and laughs like it is the most witty thing she's heard all night.

"So what's you girls' deal? You just up for the weekend, the night?"

"We're students at Arizona State and we just thought we'd come up on a whim. We actually just got here."

169

What the? Just got here, on a whim? How far is Arizona State? Like 3, 4, 5 hours from here? And they look this good? I get out of a car after a couple of hours and I look I've just woken up from hibernation. My hair's all fucked up, shirts all wrinkled, I step out of the car kicking over empty bags from McDonalds. But these girls, like I said, they are hot and look like they are ready for a big night. What doesn't make sense though, is that the night is pretty much over.

Bill grabs my arm and gives me a look like he's trying to tell me something. The dealer does the same, except he's smiling.

"Ladies, we'll be right back." Bill says as we walk over to the chip counter. Then he whispers to me, "Dude, those girls are working."

"Working? What do you mean? Like they work here?" I'm kind of confused.

"Dude, they're hookers."

My eyes get big. I get excited. "Hookers! That's awesome! I've never met a hooker before!"

"Dude, shut the fuck up!"

"Sorry," I'm whispering now, "Let's go back and talk to them. I just have never talked to a hooker before in my life. I don't even think I've ever *seen* one!"

Bill looks skeptical, "You mean to tell me that during you time in Manhattan, and actually living for a little while near Times Square that you *never, ever* saw a hooker?"

I think for a second. "Nope, not that I know of."

Bill shakes his head, annoyed, "I'm sure you saw them all the time, your clueless ass just didn't realize it."

"Whatever. Maybe I did, but you're saying those hot college girls are prostitutes? That's the coolest shit!"

"Okay, understand me Forest, one: they are probably not even college girls. Two: Unless you plan on spending some dough, they're not going to talk to us for long."

"It's not like I want to bring them back to the room, but can we at least try to talk to them and then when they get tired of talking to us, then we just leave?" I ask like a little kid at an amusement park who just wants to ride the Tilt-a-Whirl one more time.

"Fine. But they're not going to be around for long, and I'm tired."

We walk back up to the table. The dealer is still grinning his knowing grin. This little play has got to be one of the highlights of his job. Hot little 'college girls' hitting on unsuspecting 'Johns'. Then they get to the elevator, back to the room, wherever and get the old 'Pretty Woman, menu spiel'.

"Sorry it took us so long ladies, you'd think those guys can count you out a little quicker than that. Hell, it's not like we have a whole lot more money than what'll pay for breakfast." Or sex for that matter.

"I know, sometimes they can be so slow." The straight hair says as the curly hair nods again like she's never heard a more spot on observation.

"Well ladies," Bill says, "I think we're just going to grab some breakfast and hit the sack."

"We could join you if you guys don't mind?" Straight says. I guess she's the brains of the operation.

Bill looks at me with a look that says, "dude this is going too far". Almost as if he feels bad for taking up these girls' time, like at a car lot when you know you're not going to buy anything but the sales guy is spending a lot of time with you.

"Sounds good to me!" I blurt out. I just want to see how this turns out.

Curly is as excited as ever, "Great, I can't wait for some eggs!"

The four of us start walking to find a breakfast place in the casino and we can't find a one that's open. I guess the owner's idea is that shortly after late night breakfast you go to sleep and if you go to sleep you're not gambling anymore wasting all of that perfectly good oxygen pumping through the casino.

"Well, looks like we're out of luck for breakfast." Bill says in a sarcastic, less than disappointed voice. I can tell he's done with this game and ready to get out of here.

"Oh poo." Curly puts on a pouty face and crosses her arms. Straight tries her best to salvage this lost sale, "Well we could all just hang out somewhere else until breakfast places are open?"

I get ready to say that this is the best idea I've heard all night, but Bill interrupts me.

"So are you ladies workin' or what?" Arggh! I didn't know we were going to be that blunt about it. I guess his theory about their leaving when they realized that we weren't buying was wrong.

Straight looks startled and a little guilty, "Um, well, kind of."

"Sorry ladies," Bill says, "We're not in the market tonight." Curly looks like we ran over their dog. This could be for two reasons. One, if having sex is what you do for a living I'm sure you can get some pretty nasty clients. And not to blow my own horn (since you evidently you can pay to have someone else do that) but if it is your job to have sex, you could do worse than us. But to burst my ego bubble, Bill directs me to look around the room and realize that we're pretty much the only guys, or people for that matter, in the place, making us the best options simply by default.

The two girls turn and walk out the door. We look over towards the dealer at the other side of the casino. He just smiles and shakes his head as he straightens up his table. Bill and I head toward the elevators.

"How the hell do you know so much about hookers?" I ask still excited about my first known encounter with a real life prostitute at the age of 26 years old.

"Shut up. I'm tired."

The next day is more of the same. No conversations with hookers this time, but still lots of gambling, lot's of drinking, except this time we actually start to win money, good money, 'night out on the town like high rollers' money. We head up to Ghost Bar for the evening. Ghost bar is at the top of the Palms hotel and boasts the best view in Vegas. We see pictures on a post card of the balcony in the lounge and we're sold. Evidently this place is kind of hard to get into, but tonight we have the money to make it a little easier.

We get ready for the night in the hotel room, head to The Palms, and reach the bouncer at the ground floor elevator.

"Can I help you?"

"Yeah," I say, "We're going upstairs." Again, I say this like I come here all the time.

He looks at us all up and down. We're all dressed to go out. I have jeans, boots, a vintage tee and a blazer, both Nick and Bill have on their black pants, black shoes, and long sleeved button ups, so we should be good. The only problem we'll have is that we're three guys.

"It's twenty each." He says to us.

"Got it. Thanks man." I say as we slide past him to pay the girl taking money. Well that was easy.

We get out of the elevator and realize just why it was so easy. There's barely anybody here. A few people on the balcony and only two of the twenty or so tables in the lounge full.

"Well I'm going to get a drink." I walk up to the bar and lean over to talk to the cute bartender in what appears to be a leather vest with little else on. "Hey, is it always this dead?"

She looks around. "No, but it *is* Easter Sunday."

Oh yeah, I forgot. I look disappointed.

"Don't worry," she says, "The crowd will definitely pick up. Just take advantage of it and grab a table and hang out."

"Ok, great. Thanks, we'll do that."

"Great, how many bottles to you want?"

I'm confused

"What do you mean?"

"Bottles. You have to buy at least one bottle to sit at a table."

Makes sense.

"Ok, how much is a bottle?"

She pulls out a menu.

"About $300 each."

Now in any other setting, this would have been a little off putting. However, the three of us did really well at the tables today, and hey, how many times are you in Vegas. Sure let's throw ourselves a little party.

"We'll take two." I say like I'm old Blue Eyes himself and head back to what would be our 'high roller' table for the night. A couple of cute college girls come over and introduce themselves. This is going to be better than we thought.

"Ladies! Have a seat. We have a couple of bottles coming!"

Their eyes light up. The waiter brings the two bottles of Grey Goose and a tray of mixers. He mixes our first round of drinks and we all wait for the toast.

All together… "To High Rollers." The clink of the glasses is the last thing I remember clearly.

What I do know is that at some point after the club, Nick and Bill left me unsupervised in the casino.

The next morning I check my pockets while peeling my throbbing head off the carpet after waking up in my clothes on the floor of the suite living room. I find my cell phone. The call history shows calls to ex-girlfriends, my current girlfriend, my parents, and my best friend from high school. I guess I was feeling sentimental. In the other pocket I pull out an empty pack of cigarettes and three of the 700 dollars I had between leaving the club and getting to the casino. I'm convinced that if Vegas had three dollar tables, those would be gone too.

Like I said, Vegas is like sex. After 3 days straight of doing it too hard, you're more than likely going to wake up pretty sore.

Adversity, Triumph & Defeat All at Once... Err... Women

After 9/11 I actually tried, yes, *tried* to be an alcoholic. Having never been through such a life changing event, I had no idea how to deal with it. The only way I had ever even heard of people dealing with tragedy, although not recommended, was drinking. Like I said, I tried it, during the day, by myself, straight vodka on the rocks, bourbon and ginger, anything. It just didn't take. I'm certainly not complaining. I just don't know why. Maybe just like the effect genetics have on alcoholism, maybe I'm genetically predisposed to not be an alcoholic.

The time after my breakup with Julie is a different story however. Alcohol, no, *lots* of alcohol is the only way I can escape this pain. I drink as quickly as I can not to hurt anymore. I pass out, sometimes alone, sometimes not, and can't even sleep it off since as soon as the dehydration, or the call of nature to the bathroom wakes me up, my thoughts immediately return to the pain I have to deal with. The thoughts make it too hard to fall back asleep so I wake up and try to busy myself with anything, usually the gym, since it's the best way for me to get out the anger with myself on a weight bench or running furiously on a piece of cardio equipment like I'm Tracy Gold.

I read somewhere that anorexia isn't about being thin, it's about control. I believe it. I know it's hard to believe since the least I've weighed since high school is just under 200 pounds, but my behavior was a lot like that a person suffering from anorexia. I needed control, and if it meant working out obsessively, eating as little as I could bring myself to, and drinking and hooking up whenever and with whomever I wanted, then so be it. This pattern lasts a few months, making me little more than a good time party zombie. My friends start to notice.

NC State is playing ECU at the Carolina Panthers stadium in Charlotte. It's a big college reunion and my buddy Nick and I get a hotel room downtown. We plan to meet up with a bunch of people after cocktails in our room. Bill and our friend Emily meet us upstairs. Bill has a pint of Captain Morgan's Rum and Emily has a bottle of white wine, all of which is usually sufficient for an hour of drinking for four people before bars.

We start making the cocktails with the mixers in the room. I walk to my suitcase, pull out a half gallon of Jack Daniels, a tall tumbler, grab a handful from the ice bucket, and fill the glass to the top with nothing but that fine Tennessee whiskey. As I lower my glass after a swig like I'm drinking lemonade after a coming in from cutting the yard on a hot day, I notice Nick, Bill, and Emily staring at me, all with concerned faces.

"What?" I look at them and take another sip.

They look at one another, like they've talked about this before.

"Buddy," Bill starts, "I think you're drinking too much."

I am genuinely confused at his concern. I pick up the bottle and notice that I've barely made a dent in it.

"No way dude," I hold up the bottle to show it to him, "There's plenty in here." They are not amused.

Emily chimes in. "You know what he means John."

I do. I join the solemn mood in the room. "I know guys, don't worry, it's not like I do this every day." I'm lying

"Just be conscious of it dude," Nick says , "maybe just slow down a little."

"I agree guys, you're right. I can slow down. Don't worry." They don't look convinced. "Seriously! Watch." I pour the liquor in the sink. Hey, there'll be more at the bar.

We all head out for a great night, just one that's not necessarily perfect for 'slowing down'. We see people that we haven't seen in years, which leads to beers, which leads to liquor drinks, which leads to shots, which always leads to talking to girls. Luckily there's one girl in particular that we run into.

Melissa

"Hey! Melissa, right?" I act like I'm not sure of her name. In reality I've had a crush on this girl since we worked at Prestonwood Country Club together the summer between my Freshman and Sophomore year in college. I was a lifeguard and she was the stand-offish towel girl.

I had my eye on this girl at 5'3", just over 100 pounds, with big blue eyes, light brown hair, tan skin, and the hottest pouty lips for the entire summer. I flirted my ass off. Stuff that worked with most every girl at school and even one girl who I found out later dressed up to come to the pool so I would notice her. But this girl, Melissa, was none too impressed. I would smile, try to start up conversation, and do all the things a young meathead does when trying to impress a member of the opposite sex. (Oh yeah, I'm talking, the 'lean on the table, triceps/pectoral flex'. It was that bad.) I got nothing. No conversations. No smiles. Nothing. "What the?" I thought to myself. "I've got girls friggin' dressing up to come to this pool for me, and I can't get a Goddamned smile out of this one! Who the hell does she think she is?" Please understand that the level of my ego, unfortunately along with my physique, has experienced a precipitous drop since then. Now in Charlotte some seven years later, I'm a little more bearable and hopefully a little more charming.

"Yeah! Hey, John right?" I still don't believe for a second she doesn't remember my name.

"How have you been?"

"Great! I've been out in Southern California for the last few years and just moved back to Raleigh, actually!" She's smiling, flirty, and damn she is hot! I love that she's moved somewhere else and isn't another sheltered, hometown girl, that hasn't been exposed to anything outside of central North Carolina.

"That's awesome! I just actually moved back from New York and I'm living in Raleigh too. Can I buy you a drink?"

"Uh, let me think." Her face is so cute when she's being sarcastic. "Vodka tonic sounds good."

"Done. Be right back."

The official "Bar Rule Book" states: "It is still cool to buy a woman a drink at a bar. It is, however, stupid to buy all of her drinks."

I usually follow this rule to a tee, but I'm not giving this girl any reason to ditch us at this bar. It works actually, and she follows us to bar after bar, as we talk, dance, talk some more, and even stays after she starts to buy her own drinks. The night comes to an end and instead of following my recent M.O. of trying to get

this girl back home, I simply get her number and tell her I'll give
her a call sometime for us to hang out. Maybe this is the beginning
of the 'slowing down' that I've promised. Not really what they
meant, but baby steps, ya know?

Yeah, not so fast. The next night after the football game
and the post tailgating at Buckhead Saloon I find myself at the
home of this cougar that lured me there by telling me that she was
recently divorced and that I looked just like the gardener on
Desperate Housewives. Well, since flattery will get you
everywhere and booze coupled with my overactive libido will get
me most places with an attractive, willing member of the opposite
sex, I went. It's just that as soon as I got there, I just wanted to
hang out with Melissa. I go out on this woman's back deck and
dialed Melissa. Shit, it goes to voicemail.

"Hey, uh, Melissa. This is John…John Cerqueira from
Prestonwood country club. Hey, I know this sounds strange and I
know it's," I look at my watch, "Like 2:30 in the morning but I was
just wondering if you could possibly pick me up from this house in
South Charlotte. If not, uh, no big deal. I guess I'll see you
around."

I wake up on the hardwoods of Mrs. Robinson's house.
Thank God nothing happened. I guess she just wanted to see if she
could get some young punk home for the night. How the hell am I
going to get back to the….damnit! Last night comes back to me. I
can't believe I called Melissa to pick me up here. Damn the late
night calls. It is for this reason that I believe cell phones should
have an 'are you sure' prompt when making a call after midnight.

After an uncomfortable ride back to my hotel courtesy of my almost hook up in her mini van, I get back to Raleigh and give Melissa a call.

"Hello?" Oh thank God she answered.

"Melissa? It's John."

"Hey." Her voice sounds friendly like she can sense the apology to come.

"Did you have a good time in Charlotte?" She says nothing. Ok, no need for me to try small talk. "Look, I'm sorry about last night. I was really drunk and I don't want you thinking that I was expecting anything. I just didn't want to insult you like that."

"Hey, don't worry about it. You may find this hard to believe but you're not the first guy to try to call me at 2:30 in the morning and be completely ignored."

I don't know whether to be insulted or relieved. "Well hey, my roommates and I are having a Christmas party next weekend. It's going to be great. Kegs, Cosmo bar for the girls, the house will be decorated, and a bunch of people are going to be there."

"Well let me see what my friends are up to and maybe we'll stop by."

A week later and several reminder phone calls, the first party guest walks down our driveway. She's cute, little, now blonde, in a Black ¾ length jacket, a white sleeveless cashmere sweater underneath, tight pants and high heeled boots. My friends and I are on the back deck playing beer pong and kind of embarrassed that the first guest to the big party finds five drunk idiots throwing ping pong balls into cups of beer, retrieving the balls with their filthy fingers then drinking from them.

"Hey guys, can I get next game?"

Wow! She died her hair. Hot! And she came by herself! What the? Maybe she remembered the 'triceps/pectoral table lean' after all. It must just take a little longer to sink in for some people.

Rules of Engagement

Even after Melissa and I get together, I still try to maintain at least a friendly relationship with Julie, but it doesn't really work. I just don't understand people that can be friends with their ex-girlfriends.

The following December I get a call from Julie while she's on a trip in San Francisco.

"What's up kid? How are things?" Again, I hate talking to her like she's just a buddy of mine.

"Nothing, I can't talk long. You doing okay?" Let me get that right...Can't talk long, but ask how things are.

"Oh not a whole lot, just applying to B School, that's about it. Just hoping to get in. And fixing up the new house."

"Well good luck. Um..."

"Yeah, what's up?"

"Never mind. Hey, I have some friends visiting New York and they want to know where to go to dinner. Where do you recommend?" What a weird question. She's been to New York plenty of times. There's something weird about this call, I just can't figure it out.

"I don't know darlin' let me think…hmm."

"John, I have to go." I know that her new boyfriend doesn't know we talk, but why call at all? Oh well.

Two weeks later

"Good morning, John Cerqueira."

"John, hey it's me"

"Hey darling what's going on?" I get up to close my office door.

"Nothing, how are you? How's business school admissions?"

"Good, I think. I'm just getting a little nervous waiting to hear back"

"You'll be fine, I know it. I bet you charmed your way through the interview and you'll be an MBA student in no time."

"Thanks, Jules." it feels nice to talk a little more normally now. She sounds like old Julie. Concerned, genuine, sweet again.

"I have something to tell you" her tone changes, this is not good…

"Oh yeah? What's up?" My body is frozen

"John," Oh God, don't say it. I can feel it. Please don't,

"I'm engaged."

Silence. I'm speechless.

"John?"

Nothing. I can't think of a word. Any word.

"John?

Not one word

"Do you want me to let you go?"

I hang up

I pick the phone back up and dial.

"Lanier Law group".

"Yes, is Thomas in please?" I say in my daze.

"Please hold."

"This is Thomas."

"Tommy, cancel whatever you have going on tonight, we're going out."

"No can do buddy I need to…"

"Julie's engaged"

"Oh shit" he says like he's not even talking to me. "Churchills at 6:30?"

"See you there"

I spend that night in a drunken blur. It's kind of one last hurrah for alcoholic, get-over-it John. Like saying good bye one last time to the pained, desperate, shell I was a year ago. I spend most of the night hugging the porcelain, and wake up the next morning next to Melissa.

She's sleeping. Quiet. Cute. The girl I've spent the last year with happily. I realize that I'm absolutely ready to move on from Julie. No more regrets. No more what ifs. No more pain.

For the second time in my life, I realize that even the worst pain is bearable. Even the pain that is so intense that you would almost trade every happy time you ever had from a particular choice just to stop the hurting. Almost. And maybe not only does that whatever doesn't break us, makes us stronger, but it just might conquer whatever fear for pain we might have. And once we beat this uneasy fear of pain, or failure, or injury, or embarrassment, the inhibitions that keep us from doing so many things, from taking chances, what might we be capable of? Think of what we are all capable of once we eliminate that fear from our thought process when we make decisions.

What could we accomplish, how happy could we be, if we made the choice to live as if there was no consequence for making mistakes?

Back to School

My newfound motivation to realize and pursue a better quality of
life translates in no small way to my professional life and education.
After a number of sales related positions post 9/11, I decide to
pursue an advanced degree. My educational experiences from
elementary school through undergraduate studies at NC State made
it pretty unlikely that I would subject myself to any more of what I
considered mental and emotional masochism.

However, with a new lease on life, I have since made it my
primary goal to search for, identify, and pursue life enriching
activities whether they be spending more time outdoors, more time
with my family, becoming more involved within my community, or
even… yes, I'll say it… more school.

This latest idea is actually less disturbing than I would have
thought. After my senior year in college, as the last time I had
actually been required to read, I've found that I really do enjoy
reading for pleasure. Who knew? I enjoy the entertainment value
but find myself most enjoying historical fiction and stories,

including interesting factual information, and even philosophy. In other words, entertainment with a bit of an educational spin to it.

Hey, sounds like learning to me.

I also find that in my professional life, as I operate within my small scope of responsibility, my mind is starved of, ravenously craves and thrives off of new information. Throw in a canyon-deep void where job satisfaction should be and…Son, I think you just set yourself a path for grad school. . .

Attending the Kenan-Flagler Business School at UNC-Chapel Hill is now my goal, mostly due to its reputation for academic excellence and its ability to launch my career. This, combined with the relatively inexpensive tuition for residents and the proximity to my parents in the event I need money for more Ramen noodles, makes Kenan-Flagler a no-brainer. So much so that I have this goal in my sights while still living in NY, before my move back down south.

My journey to business school starts out pretty bumpy as I pick up a Kaplan GMAT book at the Barnes and Noble at Astor Place near my place in the East Village. The purchase feels like the first step on my journey to life as a fulfilled executive. Little do I know that the next few weeks will be filled with sleepless nights, stomach knots, and near anxiety attacks as I attempt to teach and re-teach myself subjects that I had supposedly been exposed to at some unidentifiable point during my academic career. I'm not usually a person who stresses, and since 9/11 I have adopted the 'what could be worse than that' attitude. However, for the first time in a while I find myself extraordinarily affected by the stress of trying to complete a test question that I may or may not be able to figure out in a half an hour, much less within the recommended time constraint of 30 seconds a problem.

After a few weeks of self study torture I decide that I'll abandon this little quest for now and pick it up 'later', with an altered strategy of course.

'Later' turns out being after my move back to Raleigh. It's June 2005 and the deadline for early action at Carolina is in October. Early action gives you a better chance of getting into school since it comes with a non refundable deposit that commits you to attending if you are accepted. The applicant pool is theoretically not as competitive since many applicants don't want to commit to any school that early. However, with Carolina as my first choice, and my lack of confidence in my intellect since my unsuccessful GMAT self study sessions, I decide that this is the way to go. This gives me just enough time to study hard for this test, take it more than once if need be, and get my application in by October. I've typically been a bit of a procrastinator so this long term planned approach is new to me. Also, In light of my lack of success with studying the GMAT on my own I decide to invest the money into a GMAT study crash course by Kaplan.

The class starts out by taking a base-line test, the test that in theory identifies areas that can be improved. For me, it was validation that I need this class no matter how much money it costs (a fine marketing ploy for Kaplan and companies of the like, if you ask me). The teacher tells us that those of us who do poorly should be excited because we can only go up from here and it reaffirms our good decision to make this class part of our application process.

This eases the blow a little, but this roses and puppies message begins to wear thin after weeks of this class and very little improvement in my score, as does my confidence.

Why do I even want this? What's wrong with keeping this same job and working hard to move up or not even moving up at all? I feel like my priorities have been in a healthier order for a while and I decided that I would place less importance on the amount of money I make and any other superficial evidence of success. So why is this test, this degree, the job after the degree so important? Who even cares?

And just as I am about to convince myself that I don't need this test, this degree, the money that comes after it and that this would go completely against my 'enjoy your life how you want it, not other people's expectation of what your life should be' theory, I snap out of it. It is as if I begin to argue with two parts of myself.

In one corner is the status-quo-path-of-least-resistance John that wants to give this stress up and continue with his job. After all, I've told myself that life shouldn't be all work and your job doesn't define you. In the other corner, the kid that my old boss from Aslan saw that he immediately wanted to hire, this kid whose desire and competency to persevere in the face of adversity was proven and refined under extraordinary circumstances. This emotional civil war doesn't last long.

Motivated by the challenge of conquering this bastard test and getting what I want, I live and breathe some of the most boring and irritating content and test taking techniques known to man until the rainy Saturday morning of game time.

My cell phone rings.

"Hey buddy," it's Bill.

"What's up man?"

"Oh not a whole lot. Hey, I'm thinking about coming into Raleigh next week, you gonna be around?"

"Yeah but I have to take that test in the morning on Saturday so I'm out of commission on Friday."

"Oh right. How's that going?"

"Well I won't know until I officially take the test, but my scores are improving."

"Well it's your call buddy, I can come another time if you want?"

"No, you know what, either way we'll go out and get shit faced that Saturday night, whether for a celebration or to drown my sorrows."

"Whatever dude. Your call. I'll give you a call closer to then and we'll get things settled. Hey buddy, good luck."

"Thanks. Later."

Let me just say now that the male gender rocks if for no other reason that our ability to have brief and concise telephone conversations.

One week later. . .

"Whoo hooo! Baby that's so great! I'm so proud of you!!" Mom yells off to the background to my Dad, "John! Did you hear how well your son did on his test?!!"

"Thanks Ma."

"Well we have to go out and celebrate! What are you doing tonight?"

"Bill's in town so the boys and I are going to go out, probably downtown."

"Ok, well how's tomorrow sound? You pick the place and Daddy and I will take you out. Bring Melissa too."

"Sounds good. Talk to you tomorrow."

"Alright, baby boy, well you be careful tonight."

Armed with a score that should give me a good chance of getting into Carolina, I finish up my application and essays and all I have left is my on campus interview. I typically come off pretty well in interviews (This guy will surely be no Oprah!) so I'm not particularly nervous, but I still do my best to prepare. I look at every resource I can about admissions interviews and what schools are looking for in applicants. I come across an article in the Wall Street Journal all about Business schools.

Holy shit! It says that Carolina is ranked #9 by top employers as to where they get their MBA employees. What the hell? I knew Carolina was a top 20 school, but number 9!?! This might be a little out of my league. I know that my GMAT was good but I've never really been a top student. Sure, I always did above average but was one of those kids who never really applied himself. This elementary school buzzword followed me all the way through high school, along with 'potential' (as in "not working up to...") and I never could figure out how the hell my teachers thought they knew what I had up in the old noodle if my grades never really showed it...

I remember signing up for AP Literature for my senior year in high school. The day before summer vacation of my Junior year my counselor called me into his office.

"Hey John, I have something for you."

"What's that sir?"

He swiveled his chair around in his windowless, public school administrators office, paused, and swiveled back around with a stack of books.

"What's all that?"

"This is your summer reading." He smiled and then frowned when he saw the expression on my face that conveyed my lack of enthusiasm for his little 'gift'.

The concept seemed as foreign as anything I had ever heard before, almost like that new term I had just learned, oxy-something or other. 'Summer' and 'Reading' just don't really seem like they go together.

"Um Sir, that couldn't possibly be *my* summer reading since, well how do I put this, I don't really *read* in the *sum-mer*." I emphasize the break in the syllables in a snotty punk teenager way hoping that he will realize what a ridiculous notion this Summer Reading really is.

"Well it is if you are going to be in AP Literature."

"Well then it looks like we'll just have to change that class then won't we? Can you take care of that for me?" Man! What a little punk. I've said time and again that if I ever went back in time to meet teenage me, I would beat my little ass!

"Are you sure John? You might find the class very interesting and your standardized test scores show that you're just not being as challenged as you could be."

"Um." I pretend to think about it for about a second. "Yeah, I'm sure. Advanced English will be fine. No reading for the summer in that one, right?"

"No John, no reading in the summer for that one." He says in the defeated way that an underpaid, underappreciated, public servant says when his only motivation for his job (the difference he could make by enhancing the lives of our nation's youth) is stripped of him by the laziness of a kid that just wants to hit the beach.

"Great. Have a great summer."

"Very well, you do the same."

This was kind of my M.O. for school. Do the minimum and use what the teacher's evidently considered to be my advanced Vulcan mind to get me by with as little effort as possible.

But this grad school thing is different. I *really* want this. I'm a different person now, one who likes a challenge, and I'm ready to work up to my potential. But…but what if my potential isn't enough? What if I try my absolute best and it's just not good enough to get what I want. I've always been okay with failing if I didn't try, but I don't think I've ever felt a failure when I've really given it everything I've got. . .

I'm Sailing. . .   I'm Sailing. . .

One of my dad's best friends, Pat, has a place down on the Jersey
Shore, not far from where my grandparent's place used to be. As
early as I can remember until my family moved to North Carolina
when I was seven, my Dad and I would wake up early and visit Pat
for breakfast. As I got older, our visits became less frequent. Later,
when my Dad and I went to visit, Pat would take us sailing on a
small wooden boat that he kept docked in the bay, about 35 yards
from his house. As a teenager who doesn't get along too well with
his Dad, this time was always like the cease fire of 'don't tell me
how to live my life' 'how are you ever going to get a job doing
that' 'don't you talk to me that way' and any other generic dad and
son stuff. When I graduated college and moved to the city, I would
take the train down during the summer to visit Pat often. During
this time, I realized that there is little in this world I would rather do
than spend time sailing.

Until I was back in North Carolina, having my own boat
didn't really make sense. Living in New York it's difficult enough

sometimes even afford your rent, much less a boat. However, within months of moving back to North Carolina, during the early spring, I found a 22 foot sailboat down in Lake Norman that I really liked. The test sail was good, the price was right, and even though I knew little to nothing about *owning* a boat, I made an offer and bought it on the spot.

After a year of having the boat on the lake I realized that wind, the key ingredient in making a sailboat move, is steady during the spring and the fall months when the temperature is changing from cold to hot and vice versa, but during the summer, the ideal time to actually *be* on a boat, the wind is nearly non existent. So without the knowledge of any other difference between lake sailing and coastal sailing, or the knowledge of how to move a boat, I convinced my father than we needed this boat at the beach.

Now I've always been kind of an impatient kid, usually neglecting to look before I leap. Luckily though, after 9/11, my new appreciation for life allows me to present any ill thought out adventures as 'taking chances' or 'trying new things to get the most out of life.' The simplest way to put it is that I want what I want when I want it.

When I bought the boat I did so with a trailer, an old rusty trailer, but a trailer nonetheless. After advice from a friend who is better versed on dealing with boats than I am, I took the trailer to be inspected and, if need be, repaired. $1200 dollars later, my $300 trailer was capable of performing it's intended duty. This is of course assuming that it would be pulled by someone with at least a limited knowledge of how to do so.

Two weeks later, I convince Melissa to help me retrieve said vessel from the lake.

"Alright kid, let's go. We'll head the three hours down to the lake get the boat, and then head the three and a half hours from there to the beach."

Melissa gets her things ready with a troubled look. "John, are you sure that you know what you're doing?"

"Of course I know what I'm doing." I'm a little annoyed at the insinuation. "How hard can it be? You see those idiot red necks at the boat ramp down at the beach. If they can do it, I sure as hell can."

She continues to look skeptical as we get in my Grand Cherokee and I put the trailer on the hitch of my truck.

"If you say so. I just don't want us…"

"Melissa!" I interrupt annoyed at her nagging, "it will be just fine." I emphasize this by saying it slowly and softly. "What do you think? I want the boat dragging on the highway?"

"Whatever." She crosses her arms in the passenger seat and pouts for the next minute as we back out of the driveway and head to the interstate.

After about 5 minutes on the interstate Melissa starts to talk to me again.

"Hey," she says sweetly, "did you want me to put in a CD?"

"Yes, that would be wonderful." I say in my best 'boyfriend trying to be nice' voice.

"OK," she flips through her CD case, "do you want, James Brown, Coldplay, Kenny Chesney…"

"How 'bout Kenny?"

"Sounds good to me."

She pulls the CD out of the case and pops it into the stereo. We head down I-40 singing along to the stereo. What a great day! Heading down to the lake to finally move the boat down to the beach. What a fun summer this is going to be, just sailing, the smell of salt water, the sun. Man, I'm in a great mood.

"Back where I come from," we sing, *"I'm proud as anyone, back where I come fr…."*

BABOOM!!!

What the hell is that!?! I look in my rearview mirror. The trailer, luckily *sans* boat at the moment, is off the ground and being pulled through the air like a kite. I can't see the hitch but I assume that the only thing holding the trailer to the truck is the safety chain primitively wrapped around the bar connecting the hitch to the truck. I see a tire fly off of the trailer and into the median. Cars behind us are swerving to avoid the mess that I'm creating. The trailer heads for the ground and bounces as high as when it was being pulled a second ago. We are swerving, and jerking from the force and I struggle to control the wheel of the car so that we don't flip and roll down the highway. Finally I am able to slow the car down and pull to the shoulder.

With Melissa and I both in a little bit of a shock and the car's antics making the CD skip to a stop, the only sound is coming from the passing traffic. We sit silent for a minute like the scene from National Lampoon's Christmas vacation where Clark avoids being crushed by an 18 wheeler by pulling off the road and hurling the family station wagon into a snow drift.

I look over to Melissa. Her face looks too scared to even say 'I told you so'. "Are you okay?"

She just looks forward. "Yeah, I'm okay."

"Sorry."

"That's okay."

As soon as I can move myself, I get on the phone with the repair shop that repaired the trailer a week ago.

"Hello, Barker Trucking."

"Yeah, hello!" I have pissy customer voice on now. "Yeah, I *JUST* spent $1200 getting my boat trailer fixed at your place and not 10 minutes down the road, the wheel pops off and this damn thing is being dragged all over the highway! Now I want you guys to tow this thing back and fix it as soon as Goddamn possible and I'm not paying a dime!"

"Sir, I'm so sorry that happened. Of course we'll send someone out as soon as possible."

"Well Thank you!"

"Sir, are you alright?"

"Yeah I'm alright! Luckily! Both my girlfriend and I could have been killed!"

"Well sir can you describe what exactly happened?"

"I already told you, one of the wheels popped off and the trailer came off the truck!"

"Can you get out and see if it broke off the axel or from the bearings?"

"What the hell do I know? I'm not a friggin' mechanic! Oh hell, I guess I'll get out and look!"

I open my door, walk around to the back of the truck and around the trailer. Hmm, that's strange. It looks like all of the wheels are attached. I look behind me down the highway. What the hell was that I saw fly off? I get back on the phone.

"Hey man, it's the weirdest thing but all of the wheels are still on the trailer."

"Sir," the guy's voice on the phone loses the humility of someone apologizing, "is your cotter pin still attached?"

"I told you, I'm not a mechanic. What the hell is a cotter pin?"

Now the voice get's condescending, "Well, Sir," the tone used to say 'sir' seems intended to make it synonymous with 'asshole,' "the cotter pin is what keeps the latch on the trailer locked so it stays on the ball hitch"

Wow, I *AM* an asshole. I feel like I'm about a foot tall.

"So you're saying it's kind of important." I try a small 'too little too late' joke to lighten the mood.

"Uh, well, yeah, if you want your trailer to stay on your truck, it sure the hell is."

"Right. Well what the hell was that tire that flew off the trailer?" I say, almost to myself.

"Well, sir (*asshole*) did you have a spare?"

I look back at where the spare used to be. I guess the tire flying off the trailer was the result, not the cause of the trailer coming detached.

"Shit." I say defeated.

"Is there anything else I can do for you *asshole*?" I'm pretty sure he actually said asshole at this point, but maybe not.

"No, I don't suppose. Uh, have a great rest of the weekend."

Hey, chalk it up to a learning experience. Sometimes in life you have to break some eggs, or trailers as the case may be. I finally got a buddy of mine to help me and after a few weekends, a few minor unexpected issues, and a little more money, the boat is now safely at the beach.

Impatience Leads to Itching

Six months after moving back to Raleigh for the second time, I decided to buy a house. I looked for a while and just couldn't find what I wanted. I was looking for an older house with character in an older, well established neighborhood. You know, with big trees, big yards, not your typical cookie cutter new construction type of place. I randomly reconnected with one of my fraternity brothers who had told me time and time again that he was a realtor and to give him a call when I was ready to buy.

I was actually just calling a number on a listing that just happened to lead me to him. But he did a good job and was working pretty well sending me to good places that I really was interested in. Unfortunately, I was having a hard time finding what I wanted in my price range and had given up for a week or so after coming down with the flu.

"Johnny C! What's up buddy? It's Champ!"

"Hey man, what's going on?"

"Oh nothing man, you back at work now?"

"Yeah, just today. This cold kicked my ass."

"I hear ya man. Well hey, if you're up for it I think I've found a place for you."

"Oh buddy, I'm still pretty beat, and I don't know if I have time."

"Well hey, I'll send you the listing over email. Take a look and let me know what you think. This neighborhood is hot so we do have a limited time to act." Man this kid is such a used car salesman.

I open up the email and take a look, it's a nice looking split-level, good square footage, in my price range, and the interior pictures look better than the last place I looked at with the puke green shag carpeting, the life sized cutout of Billy Jay Cyrus, and the smell of corn chips.

I give Champ a call back.

"Hello, this is Champ."

"Hey buddy, it's Cerqueira. You have time today to take a look at the place today?"

"Yeah man, how's 11:00 ?"

"Done, I'll see you there."

Champ and I meet in front of the house a little after 11:00 and it's perfect. Well not exactly perfect, but it has potential as a fixer upper.

"I'll take it. How do we make this happen?"

Later that day my offer is accepted and two months later I close on the house, move in, and start the Bob Vila-style transformation of my little piece of Raleigh. I start with ripping up the dirty carpet and laying hardwoods, then get Melissa to help me pick paint colors, and do a little gardening. After some time and a little elbow grease, the house is exactly how I want it...almost.

In my neighborhood the houses have kind of a little cottage feel, and some of them have vines hanging over their front stoop. They give the place a homey, lived in look that I like, so I set out for Home Depot to figure out how to make this happen.

"Welcome to Home Depot, what can I help you with." The little girl in glasses and red hair at the garden center is chipper but spacey, kind of like she has something, or nothing at all, on her mind.

"Hey there, how are you? I just bought a house not too long ago, and have been doing a lot of gardening and I was wondering if you guys had those vines that hang over the stoop of a house."

She looks up in the air for the answer. I follow her stare and realize that there are no vines where she is looking. She looks back at me and smiles.

"Oh sure we do, follow me." She leads me past a host of plants toward the end of the row. We walk almost to the end of the aisle and I still don't see anything that looks even close to vines. She leans over and picks up a small flower pot with what looks like a little sapling sticking out of it. It has a picture of a vine on it, but doesn't appear to be, itself, a vine. Despite the dissimilarity between the pot in her hand and the vine in my mind, she hands the pot to me and smiles proudly.

"Here you go!"

I look down at the pot in my hand with this pathetic little weed. I stare at it like the monkeys from *2001: A Space Odyssey* stare at that big black monolith. "Um, I don't know if you understand what I want. You see, I'd like a *long* vine," I make my arms wide to illustrate what 'long' is, "that can loop up and around my stoop." I make similar gestures to denote 'up' and 'around' now greatly resembling the confused monkeys. "Do you have anything like that?"

"Yes sir, this is it. You just have to wait for it to grow."

"How long? Like a month or two?"

"No, more like a year or two."

I smile at this poor little girl who clearly has mistaken me for a patient soul. "That's okay darlin', I'll figure something out."

"Okay, have a good day!"

Damnit! There has to be an easier way to do this, to get me vines around my door *TODAY*! I don't have a year to wait for these stupid things to grow. I might not even care about the vines by then. Where's the satisfaction in that?

I leave the store, head for home, pull onto my street and I see them. Right across the street from my house is an area of trees with vines all over them, exactly the type of vines that I want on my house! They were right in front of me the whole time! Why not just go pull these little bastards off the trees and wrap them around the overhang of my stoop? I say to myself, "Self, that's genius yet so simple. I get what I want, for free, and even better, immediately." So I head across the street to retrieve my new exterior adornments.

I begin by pulling off a piece of vine from the bottom of a tree. It comes off ever so slightly but as soon as I get about a foot of vine in my hand, it snaps. "Shit!" Ok, try again. Now I'm a little higher up the tree and I pull on the same vine a little until it breaks again. "Damn!" After three more futile attempts, I abandon my mission.

Two days later, I wake up in the middle of the night scratching like crazy. My face, my chest, stomach, thighs, and everything in between, I mean *EVERYTHING* in between is itching and bright red from scratching. What the hell is wrong with me? The next morning I walk downstairs and run into my roommate Brent. Brent is a bar tender and also in the Marine's somewhere between active duty and the reserves.

"Hey man, you probably know a lot about nature and survival stuff right?"

"Yeah, I guess. Why?" He says in between chewing bites of his bagel.

"Well man, I was trying to pull vines of some trees in the yard to decorate the house and…"

I can see his interest pique, he's curious and mildly concerned.

"Oh shit. Really?" Almost excited. What a dick. He stops chewing and flashes a big smile so I cut to the chase.

"Alright dude," I pull up my shirt, "Is this poison ivy?"

"Well if you picked your vines from the area by my truck, then I'm afraid so. If not it's either poison sumac or oak."

"Shit!"

"Sorry dude." He walks away laughing and I spend the next week and a half scratching, applying tomato juice, calamine lotion, anything, trying unsuccessfully to rid myself of the evidence of my impatience.

Moral of the story is, while I do condone the 'go for it' mentality and most acts of immediate gratification, there are certainly times when this little practice backfires. This includes, but is not limited to every decision that results in flaming itchy genitals.

Interview with the Future

I walk into the Kenan-Flagler admissions office. "Hi, I'm John Cerqueira. I have an interview with Craig... uh... " I fumble through my portfolio to find Craig's last name.

"Of course John, I'll tell Craig you're here." The 50 something receptionist with red hair, and a noticeable Long Island accent hits the intercom on her phone.

"Craig? Hi, it's Barbara Ann. You're 1:30 is here." She turns to me. "He'll be right out you can have a seat."

I unbutton the top button of my suit jacket, straighten my tie and have a seat.

After about 10 minutes I hear jovial voices coming from the hallway behind Barbara Ann and they get closer.

"Well it sure has been a pleasure meeting you. And have a great trip back to Italy."

Italy! Man, I know that the Business school is really pushing for more of an international presence. Italy!? What's a guy from Italy doing here, now? I thought this was the "early action" cake walk talent pool.

"Thank you, Craig," says Italian guy in a lightly accented voice. "It was a pleasure meeting you as well."

'It-a was a pleasure ah-meeting you as ah-well' I say in my head with a mocking Guido Sarducci accent. Man, insecurity can bring out the worst in me.

Italian guy turns to me. "Good luck *paisan*" looking down at my nametag and mistaking Cerqueira for Italian, or maybe he was just being nice. Either way I'm feeling a little nervous and insecure at the moment.

"You too, brother." I say in the most sincere way that I can muster to hide my hope that if for some reason, an admissions decision comes down to him and me, I really hope it's me.

"Ok John, you all set?" Craig says..

"Absolutely!" I say in my most go-get-'em type "A" leader voice.

"Great, follow me."

We head back to his office and nice smiling Craig shuts the door. At the same time, nice smiling Craig shuts off nice smiling Craig and is now a stone faced man in his late 40's to early 50's with what I come to learn is a military background and a reputation for a hard interview. This new Craig has my resume and is examining it for, in my mind, any mistake he can find.

After what seems like forever, Craig puts the resume down, takes off his glasses and looks up at me.

"So John, walk me through your resume." I've worked on this quite a bit. At this point I have had about 4 different jobs, with 4 different companies since 9/11 and anyone who knows about business school admissions or any job interviews for that matter knows that too many job switches in too short of time identifies a job-hopper and implies a lack of direction, responsibility, maturity, and accountability.

This is the single largest obstacle for me to get in to business school and this guy wants to jump into it right from the get go. But like I said, I've expected this and have prepared for it.

"Well Craig, you see, my first job was short lived as it was in the World Trade Center. After the terrorist attacks of '01, I decided to leave New York. Shortly thereafter, I helped an entrepreneur start up an office supply business, was offered a promotion to open an office in Chicago, but was simultaneously offered a position in Atlanta with the owner of a small consulting group. I found that suited my desire for a longer more involved sales cycle in consultative selling so I chose that company, Aslan Training.

"After a year of that, one of our clients, Getty Images, thought that since we had done such a good job training their sales people that perhaps I could sell for them, while offering further insight to their training program. So I moved back to New York to work with them in hopes of pursuing management and at some point business school. My desire for business school came quicker than I thought and I had always wanted to attend Carolina, so I decided to move back down south, gain some quantitative skills by working with Wachovia Bank doing business and personal lending and cash management, and here I am today."

Whew! I think that was one breath. Sounds air tight. I hope I don't sound like too much of a flake. The fact of the matter is, I followed jobs based on pie in the sky dreams that I was too impatient to wait for to come to fruition. The Atlanta and New York moves were primarily based on location and where I could have the most fun and enjoy my life. But this guy didn't want to hear that. At least I didn't think so.

Craig paused, hopefully to digest my little diatribe. "Well now, do you think that all of those moves to all of those companies in such a short amount of time was a wise choice? You see John, we have no doubt that Kenan-Flagler will make *you* better, but with your relatively short tenure at these companies, how prepared are you to be of value to your classmates and those people that we assign to your study groups, to make *them* better?"

Shit! He didn't buy it. He is calling me out. Have to bat this one back at him. Alright, let's you what you've got kid. . .

"I can understand how one could think that Craig. The truth is that every one of my positions has been sales related. Whether a short sales cycle with a large company selling to less sophisticated clientele, or a long sales cycle selling for a small consulting group to strategic executives. I tend to consider the diversity of the sales cycles and the clientele that I've worked with as more of an asset than a disadvantage. I have also, in my short career, been able to experience and adapt to several different types of companies, and in the rapidly changing business environment of the 21st century, I believe the ability to adapt is among the greatest skills an executive, and before that, a classmate or teammate can have. Furthermore, as shown on my resume, my ability to 'make others better' is what earned me a position to work with a consulting client that hired me based on seeing this quality first hand."

How do you like them apples buddy?!

"Very interesting. So how do you think we can help you be what you want to be?"

Great. We're on to the next question. I guess he's satisfied with my sales spin on a sporadic work history. I launch in to the next answer with more confidence.

"Well Craig, my sales background, and my most recent position working primarily with real estate based finance gives me a great foundation for real estate development, which is the area in which I would like to concentrate if we find that Kenan-Flagler and I are a good fit. After moving between New York and Atlanta for the last few years, and visiting most cities on the east coast, I see what types of characteristics enhance the quality of life in a city. I'd like to use that background, my insight, and the knowledge I'll gain from one of the nation's top MBA programs together in fulfilling a real estate development role."

The tide starts to turn and he seems like he's a little more on my side. This guy's not so bad. The thing is I can't tell if he is being nice because he knows he's not letting me in and feels bad about it, or because he is genuinely starting to like me. I try to put this out of my mind as we continue our conversation. He sees the

214

award on my resume from Senator Edwards and Governor Easley and we talk about everything with 9/11. He congratulates me but seems minimally impressed. He was a soldier, I was a suit running down steps.

"Well John, do you have any questions for me?" Now here's where I can use "sales guy" to turn this little contest even more in my favor.

"Actually there is one," he looks at me intrigued, "What type of student are you looking for?"

This is the age-old sales guy technique that everyone can see right through, yet it still most often works. It's called the 'perfect world' question. You ask the client to imagine a perfect world and list as many aspects of a product or service that they would like to have. Once they do, you pick three that relate to your product and talk about how your product meets that need. It's so simple and effective and if these business school folks like assertive leaders, let me see if I can lead this conversation a little like a sales call.

Craig answers my question with what he'd like to see in a student and I miraculously come up with examples that make me fit that description like a glove.

"So Craig," now the 'close' is on its way, "what reservations would you have, if any, with my attending this program?"

Craig looks unhappy, not uncomfortable because he's clearly running this show, but just like he really doesn't feel like answering this question. He hesitates and begins talking, seemingly against his better judgment.

"I will preface this in saying that the interview is but one of the components in the multi-faceted admissions process." Yeah, yeah, c'mon, what do you think…"But, if your scores are in order, and you are who and what you say you are, then it appears that you fit all the criteria for admittance."

Man! How non committal can you be?

"However, knowing people with your sales background and your apparent ease with interpersonal communication I often find myself wondering if an applicant might not just be telling me what he or she thinks I want to hear."

Shit he's caught me in sales guy mode and called me out *AGAIN*!

"Craig, I can assure you that is not the case here."

"So," he leans closer in what I feel is an attempt to either intimidate me or to read me, "you're saying that if you are admitted, I can expect you to be everything you say you are?"

I lean in as well, flash my most cocky smirk and in the smoothest most confident tone.

"And more."

Yes!! That's the confidence! That's the John this guy needs to see. That's the…

"Ok John, one last thing." What? What other question could he possibly have?

"Tell me something that's not on your resume."

What!?! Not on my resume!! If it has to do with me and getting into school why the hell wouldn't it be on my resume!?! What the hell else do you want to hear buddy?!

I can't think of anything better and the first thing that comes to my mind is…   "Well, uh, well. . . I like to sail." Aaagghhh! Like to sail!?! That's all you've got?

"Huh, that's nice. Well it was a pleasure meeting you." We shake hands as I realize that this isn't nearly as enthusiastic as the 'pleasure meeting you' that he gave old Vinnie Boombatz right before me.

"You too Craig, thanks for your time."

I like to sail! I like to friggin' SAIL!?! What the hell is wrong with me? What about I like to read historical fiction, I'm writing a book, anything but 'I like to sail!'

So much for the cocky approach.

I walk out of the admissions office and get a call from my mother.

"So baby how'd it go?"

"I don't know Ma. Some parts went well, but I just don't think I hit it off with the guy."

"Oh honey, I'm sure you did better than you think."

"Well, I'm not getting my hopes up."

"Think positively."

"I'm not thinking anything until December 12. I gotta go."
I say almost sulking.

"Cheer up baby, I love you."

December 12, 2005
I wake up early to check my email.

Inbox (1)

I click open the email.

From: Kenan-Flagler Admissions
To: John Cerqueira

Dear John,

Thank you for your interest in the Kenan-Flagler School of
Business for your Masters in Business Administration at the
University of North Carolina at Chapel Hill. We are pleased to
offer you admission to the class of 2008.

Well how do you like that? Working up to your potential
huh? Not a bad idea after all. Maybe I'm not as dumb as I
look…well, all right, fine, but I still got in.

Outside

Mike and I follow the crowd for a few blocks. As unbelievable as the street blowing up might have been yesterday, today I'd believe anything. The further we run, the less frightened we are about this supposed gas leak. We slow down and take a right to get off the West Side Highway and head through the West Village to get away from the mass hysteria. As we walk east, deeper into the Village, the mood becomes much more relaxed. Residents of the brownstones that line the quiet neighborhoods are in their open doorways asking passers by if we need anything. Phones, water, food, whatever we need. It strikes me as quite the contrast from the typical "rude New Yorker" stereotype known around the world.

Farther down the street, a group of 6 or 7 men and women on church steps try to get our attention. Mike and I look at the church then turn to each other with a look that says that we both think that visiting a church now might not be a bad idea. As we get closer, the people, who can tell from our physical states that we'd just come from the scene, begin to talk to us.

"Whoa, are you guys okay?"

"What's it like down there?"

We ignore the questions and begin to walk passed them up the church steps.

"We have friends at Cantor Fitzgerald. Do you think they made it out?"

This question stops Mike and me in our tracks. Mike turns to the man who asked the question.

"What floor is that?"

The man thinks for a second. "I think it's in the upper ninety's in Tower One."

Mike and I look at one another. As we both remember, the upper ninety's looked like they were above the floors that seemed the most damaged. If we had to guess, we'd say no, but neither one of us can say it. We both stare at the man, not completely shaking our head, but unable to hide expressions of sympathy and condolence. The man and the others around him recognize that our faces bear bad news. They break down in tears together, hugging each other, the message sinking in, gaining momentum and intensifying their reaction.

I turn around without a word, reach for the steel door handle, heave open the large wooden door, and hold it open for Mike. We both enter the church and stop at the threshold leading to the sanctuary.

Mike had been an alter boy as a kid but hadn't been to church in years. I hadn't been often in recent years either. We pause with a combination of emotions ranging from awe, inspired by the beauty of the stained glass illuminated by the clear sunny day, to reluctance about entering a church sanctuary embarrassed by our state of dress. I for one am wearing a cut off button up shirt with the name 'Tony' on the chest that I picked up at the service station which, the last I checked, is not exactly 'church worthy' attire.

"You wanna go in?" Mike asks.

I look to him, then back to the sanctuary. "Yeah. Yeah, for a bit." I say in a daze.

We walk forward slowly, timidly, passing pews spotted with people silent in pJayer. Several steps later I find myself closer to a church alter than I've been since my confirmation in high school. I look up to the crucifix knowing that I am in the right place, but unsure of what to do next. I suddenly realize that Mike is no longer next to me. I look to my right and see Mike light a candle. He kneels down to pJay. I look back to the crucifix and join Mike in front of the candles. I light a candle of my own and stare for a minute at the flame. It might have been more than a minute, I'm not sure because the next thing I know, I'm crippled, overwhelmed with emotion. I fall to my knees in front of the candles, hands on the floor as if I'd been kicked in the stomach. I'm stuck in this position on all fours, paralyzed by the emotional purging of fear, humility, and thanks, all lubricated by an uncontrollable stream of tears.

"Thank You God," I attempt to say out loud as clearly as my sobbing contorted mouth will allow. "Thank You, thank You, thank You." I can't think of anything else to say, but at the same time couldn't imagine anything more appropriate. I've never been as thankful in my entire life. Just an hour ago, I was minutes away from death, from never seeing my parents, sisters, or friends again. From never seeing what I would make out of myself, what type of person I would mature into, or what I could ever accomplish if I really tried. From never seeing another sunset, the ocean, or another country. From never making my life what it is meant to be. But what is it meant to be? What am I here for? How do I make sure that not one day is spent wasting a minute of this gift of life.

"What do You want God?" I'm sobbing so hard that the words come out like I'm yelling. "Anything God. How do You want me to live? What do You want me to do?"

I've never asked this question before this day. I'd never cared enough to. It's so foreign to me that it doesn't even sound like me asking it. It is so foreign that the answer is still coming to me in bits and pieces 5 years later. Sometimes I do the right thing, sometimes I don't. I try to pay attention any time He answers and I think I'm getting a little closer to understanding.

'Closer' is the key word. Hopefully I'll get it right before my time is up.

A special thanks for the support of my friends and family during the writing of this book and more importantly during the days, months, and years since that Tuesday morning some 5 years ago.

Special thanks to: Mom, Dad, Noelle, Erica, Grandma, Melissa, Mike and Jennifer, Bryan Scott, Katherine Lee, Chesley Page, Bill, Nick, TMoore, D, Newt, Pax, Salin and Karla, Skadabeesk, Cam and Whit, Benny, Todd, PMac and Sarah, Anthony V, Alicia, Tina, Jules, Em, Mike and Joy, The Delta's, Cindy, Singer, , Emily M, Yasmiin, Kathy, Dobber, Mike and Amy, Mom's "Ya-Ya's", Dad's Q-Shack Crew, Pat, Grace, Gianna, Mrs. Marinello, Tom, Tab, Doug, Skip, Firas, Lisa (Laptop), Drew, TJ, Kristy, Andrew, Andrea, Steve, Michelle, Ben, Joel, T- Roy, Laura, Mihali, and RJ.

I am lucky to have my life, but luckier to have you all in it...

Dear Reader,

As you can imagine, my experience five years ago has shaped much of who I am today. What's funny is that until I began this book, I didn't know just how true that could be. A friend convinced me that not only would writing a book about my experience during 9/11 and the five years since be therapeutic, but people might actually want to read it. Well, therapeutic isn't the least of it.

The moment I began to write I embarked on an exploration into the recesses of my mind. I had told many of the stories in this book individually for years with no emotional consequence. They were just anecdotes told at bars or catching up with friends, something to satisfy the curiosity of people interested in a story.

It wasn't until these seemingly disjointed stories began to connect that I realized how much of that day influences my life today. It was an emotional revelation much like the feeling one would get from learning more about their ancestors. The feeling of gaining even one more degree of clarity on what makes you who you are brings with it a sense of warmth and place in the world, bringing me much closer to learning not only who but what I am. Like I said, therapeutic isn't the least of it. During this process I have revealed a lot to myself and now I offer my emotional exposure to you. So if you happen to be one of the people that actually want to read it, I am honored and grateful, and I hope you can take away something helpful from my story.

This book is a recounting of events as accurately and completely as I can recollect. My candor was originally my way of ensuring that I could still make myself feel the same feelings I had in the past, that I could still connect with who I was and how I felt. The side effect is that hopefully, it actually might make for a more interesting read for you, as you can rest assured that I have pulled no punches and you are getting the whole story. However, I am sure to have failed in writing about or answering everything every reader might want to know. I mean come on, it's been a whole five years and a lot has happened.

*With that said, please feel free to write me at john@hero-sandwich.com. I would love to hear from you if you'd like to ask me a question, let me know what you think about the book, or just say 'hello'. Also, if you are a member of a book club that plans to read **Hero Sandwich**, I'd be happy to join you via telephone or, if possible, in person.*

I look forward to hearing from you and I hope you enjoyed reading my book.

-John